First Church of the Brethren
1340 Forge Road
Carlisle, Pennsylvania 17013

my heart's in the heather

my

in

heart's

the heather

EON MANLEY

unk & Wagnalls
Jew York

1

For our daughter, SHIVAUN.
And, of course, for GOGO.

BOOKS BY SEON MANLEY

Long Island Discovery
James Joyce: Two Decades of Criticism
Rudyard Kipling: Creative Adventurer
Adventures in Making:
    The Romance of Crafts Around the World
Teen-age Treasury for Girls
Teen-age Treasury of Good Humor

BOOKS BY SEON MANLEY AND GOGO LEWIS

The Oceans: A Treasury of the Sea World
Teen-age Treasury of Our Science World
Teen-age Treasury of the Arts
Teen-age Treasury of Imagination and Discovery
Merriment! A Treasury for Young Readers
Magic! A Treasury for Young Readers
Suspense . . . A Treasury for Young Adults

BOOKS BY ROBERT AND SEON MANLEY

Beaches: Their Lives, Legend and Lore
The Age of the Manager: A Treasury of Our Times

contents

my heart's in the heather

*Growing up is a journey toward a new
country where some of the laws are strange, some of the customs unusual, some of the words new; but eventually it is the
only land where for good or bad we must make our home.
All of us grow up differently and, at the same time, identically.
We are all alone, yet all part of the crowd, wondering how we
look, will we fit in, what is our tomorrow.*

*Part of our tomorrow is our past, colored by the people we
knew, the children we were, the world we lived in. We are,
as President Kennedy once said, "a nation of immigrants."
That does not necessarily mean that our parents and grand-
parents came from faraway lands; it means, rather, that the
whole structure of our society is rich with different strains,
different cultures, different dreams. Some of these different
strains in the United States have been well preserved for tomorrow; but a few peoples, the Scots, for example—perhaps*

because they are now so scattered over the United States—have rarely told their story.

Here is a part of that story—the story of a girl growing up in a Scottish-American colony that has disappeared, many of its customs and the ways of its people having been absorbed into the pattern of America. That the girl was I does not matter; what does matter is that it was a world crisscrossed with heather and hope, excitement and learning, and that we young people had the universal yearnings of young people everywhere.

Growing up is never a novel; it is a series of pictures, vignettes, in which you can capture only a part of the feelings or happenings, only a handful of the laughter or lore. Growing up is the time when we begin that pilgrimage—the hunt for our own tomorrow.

our own islands

Papa—my grandfather MacLean—came from the Scottish islands. He was vague and erratic as a Highland mist when it came to the specific.

What island, I asked. Was it Mull?

Oh, to be sure, there were MacLeans in Mull.

There were eight hundred islands around Scotland—chicks around a mother hen—and I used to sit as a child in New York City, clucking over the mystery of all of them. But was that your island, Papa? Was that where you were born?

No, it wasn't Mull.

Then Eigg, perhaps, I said. I could sit all day before the map on my desk, pinpointing dreams and fantasies in the latitude and longitude of the Hebrides.

"It doesn't matter," Papa said. "It was long ago."

"Do remember, Papa. It's not like you not to remember."

"Perhaps it's better to forget. I remember some things. The

birds, for example. Those are the important things to remember in life. The birds, the mosses, the ferns—and the everlast-
ing rock."

Papa was my rock. His past was my past. Where were my
roots? Could the map tell me? Scotland was a pink dream on
the faded water. On the chart before me, the islands stretched
like footprints, feathered by the gray, frizzy lines of hills and
mountains. North from the Lewis, south to the Sound of Jura,
and the Isle of Arran. Could it have been Barra Head? Or
Tiree? On days that I was annoyed with Papa, I decided he
came from Muck. I wouldn't muck around with anyone from
Muck. On days that Papa was patient, long-suffering, the eager
storyteller—on those days, I decided he came from Skye. Skye
was surely the most beautiful island in the whole world.

Papa was my rock; Papa was my sky; Papa was my island,
insulating me from the cold currents around me.

As a child I wanted the world to know what I knew, and I
longed to have the world tell me what it knew.

Who was I? Where did I come from? From Flannan Island
or Cape Wrath, from North Uist or Canna?

"Child, child," said Mama, "from Connecticut, of course."

That was no Treasure Island, that was no land bisected by
waters and rock, that was no place to re-create emotional geography. But it was true. I was born in Connecticut, a state I
loved and love. As children fashion themselves imaginary parents, I made myself another country. Papa's country. Papa's
Scotland.

Papa had left the Hebrides when he was a boy. Poor child,
no wonder he didn't remember. I had left Connecticut when I

was even younger. After the death of our mother, my grand-parents (Papa and Mama, we called them) and our Aunt Fiona gathered us up, raised us, and fashioned a different world for us, carved from the pavements of New York with jacks and memories, footprints and chalk. We scribbled our identities on the sidewalks and walls of the city, but I wanted to go deeper. I didn't want to be a name just scratched on the sidewalk with a piece of pink chalk.

"Seon," I had written on the pavement in front of the brownstone—"is a big stupe" someone else had contributed in the colorless declaration of white chalk. What anonymous nerve! I knew it was probably Billy Finnegan.

Billy Finnegan had an old country, he declared.

"This is an old country," I said. "The United States is far, far older than anybody can remember."

"Well, it's not as old as Ireland," Billy Finnegan said. "Not as old, not as green, not as beautiful. Yes, and the water isn't as blue."

"Who told you?" I asked.

"My mother," said Billy.

"What does she know about it?"

"She was born there," said Billy. "So there!"

Jimmy McNamara had an old country, too. The sun shone brighter, the lakes glistened in the sun, the flowers bloomed like the Virgin's jewels.

"And you know what?" he said.

"What?" I answered, lowering my voice because of his somber seriousness.

"The apple trees always bend from bowing to the Virgin."

"Where?"

"In Ireland, stupid."

"Who told you?" I said.

"My father," said Jimmy.

"Oh," I said. "I guess he was born there?"

"You bet," said Jimmy. "Everybody important was born there. Al Smith, Jimmy Walker."

"That's silly," I said. "That's not true."

"That's because you're jealous," said Jimmy. "You don't have an old country."

I *was* jealous. Who was I? What did I have? I had no mother. My father was far away in Connecticut. But worst, worst of all, I had no old country. Only a new one; a fresh new sparkling world that was all around me. A world of islands.

First there was the island of Manhattan itself, all the way from the old Aquarium up to the Bronx. Then there was the smaller island of our own neighborhood, which extended, at the very most, ten blocks; yet surely within those blocks was the universe itself.

When I grew up, I discovered that James Joyce, that man old Mr. MacQueen talked about in his Saturday afternoon "Chats about Writing Chaps" (no mention of writing ladies) in his Pan-Celt Bookshop in our neighborhood, had used Dublin as representative of the world. Too bad, I thought, Joyce did not know our streets in the late twenties and thirties. After all, Dublin had only the Irish. We had the Scots and the Irish —a proper Pan-Celtic stew, Mr. MacQueen said. The neighborhood was further spiced with a few Italians, flavored with a few Armenians, and stirred occasionally with a firm one hundred percent American hand—Mama's more likely than not. It was a heady diet of wild conversations and cultivated customs.

And there was the island of our own block. Our block was primarily Scottish and it extended from Central Park West to the Hudson River. The Scottish families were as clannish, self-protected, and self-protecting as they were in the Highlands years ago. We children did not attend public school, but went instead to the Scottish school where, my aunt said somewhat belligerently, "they give the pledge of allegiance to the flag of Robert Burns."

On both sides of the thin plaid line of our street, the "Irish streets" flowered in a beautiful way that we Scots could not approximate.

But together, Scots and Irish, we made a neighborhood, impregnable, impetuous, even imperious. The brownstone houses stood, I imagined, like great Gaelic castles. If they did not look down upon the Firth of Forth or upon Galway Bay or on the coves of Little Minch, they were nonetheless glorious citadels. There were two apartment houses on our street, but they were alien soil altogether. We knew none of the people who lived there, and they, I'm sure, did not care that around them teemed the past. They were surrounded by a Celtic culture that propagated completely different children—the Scots and Irish. And by a different language, Gaelic, almost forgotten but lurking still in the agreeably harsh, yet melodic eternal street conversations—but there again the intonation between Dundee and Donegal was as different as Brooklyn and the Bronx.

We were an island of rigid religions. For their part, the Scots, inflexible with the high heart of the Highlands, stiff, acrid as moss; the Irish, softer, I always felt, with softer waters shining in their eyes, softer rain falling on their ancient history and a softer dew on their Church. Those islands of Presbyterianism and Catholicism were joined on our streets into a peninsula made out of the volcanic ash of the past. No street gangs ever emerged, but our street rhymes are famous. Our jump ropes were tied to the corners of County Antrim, to faraway John O'Groats, to the streets of Edinburgh, Glasgow, Belfast, and Dublin. We jumped each day into the future, but our language echoed with the past.

The Scots and the Irish had been fortunate that they had the English language. English had separated them from the rest of that great wave of European humanity, sometimes inarticulate and lonely, which surged upon the shores of the New World.

We were an island of friendship. Papa's friends, like the brownstones themselves, were castles of the past. They had long and mysterious corridors in which their stories rattled around like ancient pieces of armor.

There was Mr. Frazer, pale as a ghost, I thought, and on that ghostly face his eyebrows twitching away like question marks above black, doubting eyes. Those eyes had seen everything—or so he said. Those eyes had seen the heather when he was a boy, and they had seen the great iron pots (I saw those pots instantly; surely they were what the witches used in *Macbeth*) in which his mother boiled all the dyes for the old tartans. Those eyes had seen the broom and the islands lost in a fog of hope, where Prince Charlie stretched his heart for comfort.

Those eyes had seen the bed of Flora MacDonald; those eyes had seen the misery of the Gorbals in Glasgow as well as the princely city of Edinburgh. Those eyes had seen the great books of the Gaels.

If Mr. Frazer was all eyes, then Mr. Ferguson was all tongue. His tongue wheeled and cavorted like the spring light on the waters of Loch Ness. He carried a covey of tales the way a hunter would shoulder a brood of partridge. He knew the story about the Smith's Rock in the Isle of Skye. He knew the story of the strong man of the wood who was twenty-one years on his mother's breast (we were shocked and titillated by that ancient traditional tale), and he knew the story of Finn's journey to Lachlan. We gloried in the terror of his tales, savoring the legends that had frightened and entranced our ancestors in front of the hearth generations ago.

We heard with Ferguson's voice, we saw with Frazer's eyes, and all the time we children, a handful of us in the streets of Manhattan, grew more and more American as we were rubbed against the abrasive emery paper of another culture. That was the way the United States was sharpened; it was the way in which our country was smoothed and varnished into a culture peculiarly its own.

In the streets of our island the Celtic folklore flourished. I learned later that there were other islands in the city: Greek, Italian, German—even more. Each had different stories that whipped across the children's consciousness before they went to bed. Different islands, different dreams, yes, even different ideals sat beside the children; different voices hummed different lullabies and different tables gave up different foods.

24

We were islands of our own folklore, those rites of passages, of life and birth and death. There were those charms of Mrs. Dolan's—one against the whooping cough: "Columbine put it to his heart and to his side and to his bosom to banish the powerful whooping cough."

Yes, Mrs. Dolan's was against the whooping cough, and Mrs. Finnegan had one against an aching tooth. It was a charm "which Mary sent to her son in the door of the City of Christ against maggot, against ache, against worms in the head."

And old Mr. MacAndrew had one which he smoked after his pipe. He tugged on that prayer more fiercely than he tugged on the briar clenched in his teeth. He intoned it, polished it, smoked it, enjoyed it, and spit it out while we children listened.

"May not more numerous be the grains of sand by the sea, the blades of grass on the lea, or the drops of dew on the tree, than my tobacco is to me."

There was the island of my own childhood friends—Johnny MacDonald, dark and fast, nervous with his childhood, throwing his young arrogance around as he dashed balls against the wall that said "No Ball Playing." There was my sister Gogo. The two of us were almost a continent—two small islands joined together to grow up in a sea we did not fully comprehend, in the strange archipelago of our family.

Mama was all American, further back than the Indians, said Gogo. Much, much further back. Papa was all Scot. Because they were our grandparents, we telescoped a generation. We circumvented some of our childish pains about our mother's death, and learned to walk again in a different culture. We stumbled at first, but then gained the solidity of brownstone porches, the lilt of friendship's voice, and an island of the past which we would never have attained in any other way.

It was a magnificent old country.

sunday's lasses

At first we stumbled through a different language. Oh, yes, the Scots spoke English, but the fathers of other children in the park on Sunday did not call out:

" 'Farewell the glen sae bushy, O!' "

Papa's voice rang through in the crisp January air, skipping and cavorting in sharps and flats. Once more around the reservoir and we would have completed our Sunday constitutional.

" 'Farewell the plains sae rushy, O!' "

"What's 'sae bushy, O,' Papa?" I asked.

"You haven't lived, lassie, until you see the bush and bracken of the Highlands."

"There's lots of bushes right here," said Gogo, pulling at my hand. "Let me go. I can walk by myself."

"Mama said . . ." I began.

"I don't care. I can walk by myself."

"Okay, fussy. Go ahead. You're a pest. And what's so rushy, Papa?" I asked, turning my attention back to his walking song.

"Little Gogo's rushy," said Papa. "She's rushing to grow up, aren't you, Gogo?"

"It's not that kind of rushy, Papa. I know that. Don't tease."

"Well, you've seen them in the country. There are rushes of all kinds down by the train tracks."

"Cats' tail," said Gogo in instant comprehension. "Those are cattails."

"We called them rushes," Papa said.

"Mama calls them cattails," Gogo said. "Aunt Fiona calls them cattails, too. Uncle Jamie calls them cattails—everybody. Rushes is foreign."

"Are, are, are. Don't say is," I said.

"Is, is izzy. Seon is crazy," sang my sister.

"Make her stop, Papa. She's always saying awful things."

"Yellow-bellied cockroach."

"See what I mean, Papa. That's her favorite expression."

"Have you ever seen a yellow-bellied cockroach, Papa?" Gogo asked quite seriously. "Have you ever seen one all stretched out dead with a yellow belly?"

"Lots of girls have *nice* little sisters." I sighed.

"I don't," said Gogo, giggling. "I don't. I don't. But I've got a yellow-bellied cockroach for a big sister."

Farewell, the plain sae rushy, O!
To other lands I now must go,
To sing my Highland lassie, O.

"I'd like to go to the other lands," I said.

"Most Scots do," said Papa. "It's a funny thing. There's no people more loving to their own home and hearth. Yet give them an even chance and they're off to the corners of the globe."

"Globe means earth," said Gogo.

"That's right," said Papa. "Do you remember how we spin the globe and look for Scotland? Do you remember, Gogo?"

"I know where New Jersey is. Don't I, Seon?" She was growing tired, I could tell. Papa shouldn't quiz her so much. She was too little.

"Hold my hand, Gogo," I said.

"Okay."

"It's a fine day," said Papa. "How was Sunday School?"

"I learned the books of the Bible," Gogo said.

"My goodness. That was a lot to learn."

"Genesis," said Gogo. "Lifidus."

"Not Lifidus, Gogo," I corrected her. "Leviticus."

"You sound like Aunt Fiona," Gogo said.

"No I don't," I told her belligerently. "I sound like me. Don't I, Papa?"

"Of course you sound like you," said Papa, "and Gogo sounds like Gogo and your grandmother sounds like your grandmother."

"And Aunt Fiona sounds like Aunt Fiona, doesn't she, Papa?"

"Indeed she does, lass. Fiona surely does sound like Fiona."

"Papa sounds different," said Gogo. "Papa's foreign."

"Why do you keep saying that?" I cried.

"Don't get mad, Seon. I'm littler than you."

"You're meaner."

"No, I'm not. I'm not, am I, Papa?"

"Of course not, child. . . . But you shouldn't keep saying I'm foreign."

"Aunt Fiona says . . ."

"Now you don't have to quote Fiona to me."

"She doesn't like the Scots," I mentioned.

"Does she like me?" Gogo asked.

"Of course she likes you," I answered. "You're her favorite. You're her baby. I guess I'm just a nuisance to her."

"You're a yellow-bellied cockroach," said Gogo sweetly, regaining confidence in herself.

"I bet," I said, drawing myself up to my full height and superiority of two years, "I bet you don't say that in Sunday School."

" 'To sing my Highland lassies, O,' " sang out Papa.

"That's us," said Gogo, putting her hand into mine. She certainly could look sweet when she wanted to. "That's us. We're his Highland lassies, O."

the tongue of exile

"Ridiculous," said Papa. "Of what conceivable value could Gaelic be to any child in New York? Really, MacCollough, these glens of Manhattan have their own tongue."

"Street urchins," moaned MacCollough. "Our children are turning into ragamuffins. Every time I see them playing marbles, I see them denying our ancient culture. Where is the Highland spirit? Where is that courage, that valor? Where is our mother tongue?"

"Don't burn it on your tea," said Mama sharply, as she sat the brown pot on the corner table.

"I'm head of the Children's Feis, Mrs. Mac," said MacCollough, "and we've got a jolly program planned."

"Better than last year, I hope," said Mama. "Half of the children reciting had no tongue at all. It's strange to me, Mac-

Collough, why you think it's easier for children to forget in two languages instead of one."

"You're no Scot, Mrs. Mac," said MacCollough. "In this instance, you'll have to excuse us. Highland blood runs deep and strong."

"And Highland tongues run fast and wild," said Mama. "Well, I'm going to the pork store. Are you coming, Seon?"

"I want to hear about the Feis," I said.

"Suit yourself. But how to select a loin of pork may go a bit further than a Gaelic lesson."

I had no desire to learn Gaelic. But I was eager to hear about the Feis. I had a secret desire that I had told no one—not even whispered to Gogo when we were supposed to be asleep, not even revealed to Papa in our intimate moments of companionship, not even to Mama in that rush of love that came mixed up with growing rebellion.

Each age has a new longing. Each age has its own rhythm. Each age knows it can express itself only in one glorious undertaking. Surely they could see it in my eyes, I told myself. Surely they could see it in the way I walked. Surely this year I would be chosen.

I wanted, yes, more than anything in the world, to be a Maiden of the Moor. The very idea would have shocked Mama and Papa, and in my dreams, I kept the longing as close to me as a blanket. I knew all the steps, all the timing, all the gestures. I could see myself kilted and shawled, with buckles on my shoes, swaying and leaping through the intricate choreography of another culture.

Each year Miss MacBride chose four girls to be Maids of the Moor. They would become the partners of the previously selected Highland Lads, and together this mixture of innocence and romantic names would, as Papa said, emerge as a Highland Charleston.

"That's the rub," said Papa. "It's not, lass, that I've any objections to your dancing. You're graceful enough. And you know your left foot from the right foot. Certainly you wouldn't think that Miss MacBride would find *that* impossible to teach."

"I like her, Papa."

"Aye, lass. You've a generous heart. But believe me, you cannot learn the Highland sword dance on the sweet crushed heather of Brooklyn Heights."

"Miss MacBride isn't from Brooklyn," I said glumly. "She's from the Bronx."

"Oh, is she now?" said Papa. "From those great stag-ridden stretches of the Park, from the home of the red deer and yellow moon."

"You're teasing."

"No, lass, I don't mean to tease you. But we carry these traditions too far. What I want you to do is preserve the best. There is a Highland spirit, you know—much as your grandmother may spurn it. There is a Highland courage . . . But, why, lass, should courage and spirit be perpetuated in a war dance? That's all the sword dance is—a war dance, primitive, bloodthirsty, wild."

"It's old," I said. "If it's old, it must be good."

"Lass, what nonsense is that? It's old, all right. Old enough

36

to know better. If it's a choice between the Gaelic and the sword dance, it will be the Gaelic for you," said Papa.

And that, Papa stated, was ridiculous enough.

"Besides," added Papa as an afterthought, "it's not an appropriate dance for girls."

I brooded about the unfairness of life for a long time. It was just like the peacock and the peahen. The peacock could strut and storm in a frenzy of glorious feathers, each mottled and tipped with an array of colors. The peahen was as dull as a brown school uniform, straight and withered as an autumn poplar. It wasn't fair. There was no justice in the world—for Papa never once let us wear the kilt.

"The kilt is a man's garb," said Papa. "If you want a pleated skirt out of the tartan, all right, but the kilt you'll have to leave for your son. And that's what I plan to do, my lassie—leave my kilt that my father left to me to your first son."

"It will have moths by then," I said defensively. "Besides, American boys hate kilts."

"Oh, do they now?" said Papa. "Tongues say one thing—blood says another. Watch them at the Feis. Every boy there in a kilt feels the winds of the Western Sea slapping against his thighs."

I had my own ideas about the drafts in the damp church basement where the Feis was held. Maybe they were the winds of the Western Sea to Papa, but I secretly agreed with Mama that the holy Caledonian dampness that gripped at the bowels of the church was a touch of Papa's Scotland that needed a good airing.

"The Scots love a gray day," said Mama to Mrs. MacDonald.

"It's easy enough to marry a man you love," said Mama, "but you should also be climate wedded. If you like the sun, so should he. But the sun's not for a Scot, after all—eh, Mrs. MacDonald?"

"Mrs. Mac," said our neighbor, "a Scot's one thing. A New York Scot's another kettle of tea entirely."

Even Papa agreed that was true.

"They're idiots," said Papa, "trying to turn Gaelic into a modern tongue. The Scots and Irish are idiots that way. And the New York ones are the worst of the lot. They'll hang onto the past like a dog with a bone—even when the bone is rotted to dust like the past in the mouth.

"The truth is," added Papa sadly, "we're tied to the past long after the past has loosened its reins on us. And the immigrant is the worst of all. With his kilts, with his bonnets—and," he snorted, "his Gaelic.

"How much Gaelic do you suppose they're speaking in the streets of Edinburgh today—eh, MacCollough? Answer me that."

"Look what the Irish have done," said MacCollough. "It's a glorious thing to hear an ancient language declaimed throughout the Senate. It was my pleasure and honor to hear William Butler Yeats himself in the Irish Senate."

"Speaking English, I'd remind you," said Papa.

"Well, what's this about Seon and the Gaelic? It will be exciting, lass," said MacCollough, turning to me. "When you learn to speak a tongue that your ancestors spoke, some part of you keeps aflame the very fire of the past. Now what I've got in mind, Mr. Mac, are two fine recitations. I'll coach my young

Malcolm in the one. And a fine, bloodthirsty one it is, too,"
said MacCollough with relish.

"Can we wear the kilt?" I said, interrupting.

"Malcolm will," said MacCollough. Then, seeing my disappointment, he added, "But you'll need some new patent-leather
shoes—with your best silver buckles, mind you—and Mrs.
MacCollough's dress shawl. What about that now?"

"She'll wear her own tartan," said Papa. "We'll get a dress
shawl ourselves."

"Good," said MacCollough. "Good, lass. Now . . ." And
his voice started a series of lessons that droned on and on, in-
toning, demanding, declaiming, discovering a language that
sang, sobbed, celebrated stories so ancient that I sat for hours
spellbound.

This was the immigrant's catechism. Mr. MacCollough, a
wisp of a man, took on new shape. He had the strength and
courage of Fingal. He had the age and wisdom of Ossian.

"Is mise Conloach Mac-nam-con," he shouted, and I be-
lieved him. He was Conloach, son of Cuchullin. Imagine, I
thought to myself, the great heroes of long ago walking the
streets of Manhattan. I could see the soft hillocks of Central
Park peopled by giants of yesterday. I could hear their voices
pierce the rumble of the traffic:

More numerous than the dewdrops on the grass,
Were the ends of arteries cut on Finn's thigh . . .

I began to practice on Mama at teatime.

" 'Agus chad' mise ach in air erleig.' " I tried out an old
adage.

"In English, miss."

" 'I have nothing but butter on a live coal.' " I laughed. " 'Porridge in a basket, and paper shoes.' "

"You'll get nothing but the back of my hand," said Mama.

In two months we were ready for the Feis.

The Children's Feis was held each year in early March. Mama said that was why the month always "came in like a lion"—because the young people, excitement at a creative fever pitch, were like caged beasts as they perfected their recital pieces.

The recital was held in the basement of the church house. The walls, we performers felt, were gorgeously decorated. Hung from them was every plaid blanket, shawl, coverlet, and tartan spread that the community could provide. It looked to me as mysterious as one of the store-front palmistry stalls that the gypsies sometimes inhabited for one brief glorious day on Amsterdam Avenue.

Mr. Frazer's staghead graced one end of the hall. It was frightening in the Frazer living room but, here in the hall, it was dwarfed to the size of a pet. The small children stood on the chairs and petted its nose and gave it offerings of scones and honey. At the other end of the hall, the great tables, magnificently embellished—Mrs. MacCollough had attempted to dye some carnations plaid—were burdened with the wealth of the kitchens of the community: bannocks, scones and muffins, Dundee cake, oatmeal cookies, heather honey and jams, and great enamel pots of tea.

The church basement seemed cavernous to us that evening

—the lights more exciting than Christmas, the richness of the evening (surely, it seemed to us children, it must be after midnight, even though the clock said nine-thirty), and the passions of old ritual and old friends storming and stalking through the hall like ghosts and spirits of the past. Or, rather, they were jigging, because the dancing was already underway. It has never ceased to amaze me that the Scot, tempering all speech and deed, when faced with the lament of the bagpipe and the curlew cry of the fiddle, will cast aside all concern and dance, cavort, canter with rhythm so deep that it seems a step is never learned, but that toe and instep, ankle and thigh explode into a rhythm that is wedded to moors and heather, rocks and sand, furze and firmament of just one land:

SCOTLAND!

The dancers were our closest neighbors, our dearest friends, and yet, as I watched them, their secrets were not mine. Their past was so long ago and far away that I could not imagine what their childhood must have been in a country thousands of miles away in a world as old as time:

SCOTLAND!

What was it really like? Or was only memory now their old country?

Soon the entertainment began. I held my breath as the Highland Lads and the Maids of the Moor explored the intricacy of the sword dance. Papa was right, I decided—the dance was quite inappropriate for a girl. And beshawled as I was with a MacLean tartan tight across my shoulders, with my blue serge skirt sharpened into creases as taut as my stomach, and with my patent-leather shoes with great square silver buckles that had belonged to my great-grandmother, I was, I decided, far, far more than a Maid of the Moor. And when my turn came to perform, I stood, with Papa's pride, my backbone, and Scotland's past on my tongue:

Siol Cholla is Chuinn thu
Mo mhire bhog bhirn thu

MacCollough had taught me well. It was one of the oldest Gaelic poems, a lullaby:

Of the race of Coll and Conn art thou
My cause of merriment, soft and sweet art thou

I felt that rush of glory of the performer. The words held my audience, and I crooned them to my own dreams, rocked them to my childish bosom:

My soft cause of merriment.
My knee has brought you up.

I wondered as I said the words how many of the familiar faces before me—the MacKenzies and the MacDonalds, the Fergusons and the Stewarts, the Campbells and the Frazers—had heard that same verse as a child. Their knees had brought me up, their tongue was my tongue, and, although it might be rough with exile, it was soft with memory. Somehow, through all of them, I had learned the language of love.

42

our black, fierce city

The trouble with New York City, said Johnny MacDonald, contemplating the long vista of our street, was that you could never get the proper ingredients to make frog's bread.

"Mama makes good bread," Gogo said, "every day."

"She certainly doesn't make frog's bread. For frog's bread, you need a great big healthy frog." He waited silently for this to sink in. But Gogo, who could play easily with frogs, tadpoles, small fish, and any other animal that lived or crawled, was unimpressed.

"When the old people left Scotland," said Johnny, conspiratorially, having made no success with his slimy frog conversation, "if they didn't carry a piece of decent frog's bread, they died before they reached their destination."

"Maybe we could get a frog in the park," said Gogo. "How do you make this frog's bread, anyway, Johnny?"

"My Da told it to me," said Johnny. "He told me it might
stand me in good stead. I thought I just might give the recipe
to you girls, because you're going to the country. If you had
some frog's bread, you could make the trip very easily. But
maybe—maybe best of all—you could send me back some
frogs in a box or something like that. Could you, Seon? And I
could make my own frog's bread for Uncle Timothy."

"Who's Uncle Timothy?" said Gogo.

"Uncle Timothy," said Johnny, "is my second cousin on my
mother's side. His mother was a Frazer."

"Can we eat peanut butter on that frog's bread?"

"No, Gogo, stupid. It's not really to eat, anyway. It's more
like magic. That's what my Da used to say happened. When his
family came down from the Highlands and settled in the city,
they were always careful that they carried with them a little bit
of frog's bread. But now, my Da says, when people leave Scotland and come over here, they forget all about it, and that's the
reason they have so much trouble when they get here. That's
why they don't have a chance to get a job at all, and have to do
what Uncle Timothy has to do. He's going way out to California to try to make his living."

"Is he going to discover gold?" said Gogo.

"I imagine," mused Johnny, "if you had yourself a really
good piece of frog's bread, you could discover anything. It's
real perfect magic. Maybe my father would let me come down
to the country with you girls, and we could make up a whole
mess of frog's bread."

"Could you use something else instead?" said Gogo. "Blue-
fish, maybe, or a little bit of haddock. Why don't you ask Mr.

Murphy, the man in the fish store? Maybe he could get you some frogs."

"The important thing," said Johnny, "is they have to be real country frogs. Who ever heard of getting any magic from the fish market, anyway?"

"Papa swears fish is brain food," I said. "Maybe that's what happens about the frogs. And if you eat a lot of brain food, you know how to take care of yourself in perilous situations."

"My Uncle Timothy," said Johnny, "isn't in a perilous situation, but he certainly is out of work. I think it's awful to live in the city, anyway. I think you're both lucky to go away every summer."

"The city's nice this time of year," I said.

"It won't be soon," said Johnny. "It will be hot and awful, and there will be those pictures in the paper of frying eggs on the sidewalk. But every time I try to fry an egg on the sidewalk, some cop comes along and tells me to beat it. Besides, it doesn't work, anyway. They smear, and run, and get all over your clothes. It seems to me that the men who take those pictures for the newspapers must live in a different world entirely, as my Da says."

"Did you ever think," Gogo said, "of trying to catch some frogs in the lake in Central Park?"

"No self-respecting frog would be seen around here," said Johnny. "Frogs like the country. I like the country, too, and I don't know what there is about my papa and your papa and all the men that live around here that they like the city so much. You know, when I grow up, I'll be a farmer."

"Like Robert Burns?" I said.

"No, just like a plain, ordinary farmer. I feel sorry for those farmers, though," said Johnny. "Look what happens to their land. A big wind blows, and it blows, and blows, and it blows the state of Oklahoma right off the map. It's nothing but a pile of dust, I bet, now. I bet it isn't even there. I bet if you go over in an airplane, there would be just a great big hole there."

"Sometimes," said Gogo, "when there are cyclones, lots of things get sucked up in the air. I bet frogs could get sucked up in the air. I bet if we stood here on the street corner long enough and it started to blow a good wind, we could look up and frogs would come flying right through the air, and you could just reach up, Johnny, and get one and we could make ourselves a mess of frog's bread."

"You shouldn't tell Gogo things like that," I said to Johnny. "She gets an idea fixed in her head and she'll just stand here until it gets dark, and I'll have to cover up for her and say we were visiting Mrs. Dolan, and we brought her some flowers from one of the street carts because she was sick. Instead Gogo will just be standing here trying to catch some frogs that are never going to come flying through the air."

"Well," said Johnny, "maybe she will find some. After all, those frogs jump. You read about it in Mark Twain—about that jumping frog."

"Jumping isn't flying," I said. "I don't see how you got frogs on the brain, anyway, Johnny.

"Gogo," I shouted, "you stay away from that dirty gutter. Mama told you not to go so close to the street."

We moved over to the edge of the street with her to see what she saw—little pieces of dirt, paper, and gum wrappers washing down the stream of city life into the waiting, opened vents of the sewer underneath.

"I bet," said Gogo, looking down into the vents, "I bet there are more frogs there than you can imagine. I wonder if I put my ear against it, whether I couldn't hear them?"

"You'd hear nothing but gurgling pipes," I said. "That thing is full of germs."

"I like city rivers," said Gogo. "This is a little tiny river. See, it's no more than two inches wide, but I bet it stretches millions of millions of miles."

"Well, I don't bet it does," I said. "They were just washing the streets up on Columbus Avenue, and this is nothing but a little leftover water coming down."

"I like the city," said Gogo.

"I like the country," I said. "I wish we could go to the country and stay there forever and ever."

"The Scots," said Johnny, "have never been helped by the country, my Da says. If it weren't for the cities," said Johnny, "we never would have had a man like Keir Hardie or John MacLean."

"They were nothing but politicians," I said. "That's what my Uncle Jamie claims. It doesn't matter whether they're Irish politicians or Scottish politicians, they're all politicians."

"Do you think politicians have a lot of money?" Johnny asked. "I bet I know how they could get it."

"How?" said Gogo. "Making frog's bread?"

"No. Catching bumblebees. My grandmother told me that. You catch the first one you see in the spring and you put it in your pocket and you treat it very carefully, and you can be very sure you won't be out of money until the next spring."

"Let's go to the park, then," said Gogo. "You don't see any bees here, but I bet you see them in the park. Do you think, Johnny, maybe we could gather a whole pocketful of them and we could sell them for real money?"

"You take everything so seriously," I said to Gogo. "I've never seen frogs down this sewer."

"You never see anything any more," said Gogo. "You think you're old. You don't want to play with me any more, I know that. Well, I can always play by myself and get my own bumblebees and my own frogs."

"You can't do anything like that. Mama said I had to stay close to you."

"I wouldn't need you," Gogo retorted, "if I got some frog's bread. I wouldn't need you if I got a bumblebee, because I could give somebody a nickel and they could cross me on all the streets and I could go to the park by myself. I could even go way downtown to see Papa, and I could get on the train by myself and go to the country any time I wanted to. All I need is a couple of bumblebees. Besides, maybe a real bumblebee would be better than you. It would buzz, buzz, buzz, instead of yell."

"I don't yell," I said quietly. "I do try to reason with you. That's what Papa says I should do, reason with you."

"You're the reason I got a headache," said Gogo belligerently.

Johnny began to chant at the top of his voice:

Oh, it's I have the headache,
A gum boil, a tummy ache,
A pain on my left side,
A pimple on my tongue,
A hip, hip, hurray.

"Come on," said Gogo. "I'll skip you to the corner."

Our feet, voices, and fantasies hammered on the pavement. I did not know that we were "tradition" carriers—that those Edinburgh, Glasgow, and Dublin street rhymes had come over the water in family satchels of childhood memories, and that they were then stored in that great old steamer trunk of culture that was the American heritage.

Charlie, Charlie, Chuck Chuck Chuck,
Went to bed with two old ducks.
One died, the other cried,
Charlie, Charlie, Chuck Chuck Chuck.

"Playing with the girls again, Johnny," said Mrs. Finnegan, as she strolled by. Johnny stuck out his tongue behind her back.

"Boy," he said, "if I had some frog's bread, I'd run away myself."

the taste of independence

Once a year we went to Molly Pitcher's Well. This was our one traditional family excursion. It generally occurred shortly after the Fourth of July, and it is still associated in my mind with open fields of freshly cut green grass, the patriotic confusion of fireworks and flags, and the exotic pleasure of fried-egg sandwiches. In those days of our childhood, however, it was anticipated by my sister and me with painful anxiety as well as pleasure. "Togetherness" had yet to be invented, but we could sense that the warm, everyday affection between Mama and Papa dissolved in the heat of the more intense emotions provoked by the day's outing.

Papa simply did not share Mama's enthusiasm for Molly— that gallant heroine of the Revolutionary War. She had been the first star in Mama's life, and I acquired her in due course, a worn-out fantasy but still colorful, appealing, inspiring. Patriotism and picnics are apt to be afflicted by the mites of dissen-

sion. Mama's "Americanism" and Papa's "Scottish backward-
ness," as Aunt Fiona said, "were two slices of bread between
which we children were firmly trapped." Our journey to
Molly's Well often flared up into outright resentment.

"I sometimes think," Mama complained, "that your grandfather is downright impossible. He's been in this country a lifetime, but he's still a Scot.

"Oh, well," she always concluded, defeated by her own in-
sight and tolerance, "you can't erase a country when you erase
a burr. His accent's different, but his soul is the same. A Scot's
soul!"

Mama rarely spoke this way, but I could understand her
feelings. This journey to Molly's Well was an American pilgrimage. In some curious fashion, Papa, completely adaptable
in all other ways, did not fit in. Once a year, he was all Scot,
and the rest of us painfully American. I was proud, proud of
Molly. All of Monmouth County, New Jersey, perpetuated her
story. Her name was blazoned on hotels and tearooms. I con-
jured up a picture of her—a little of Joan of Arc, a dash of
Barbara Frietchie, and a good deal of Martha Washington as
portrayed by Gilbert Stuart (a portrait forever fixed in my
mind by the courtesy of the Monmouth County Coal Company's annual calendar). I told myself her story over and over
again. How Molly had stood firm and impassive during the
bitter battles that had sucked the countryside around Freehold
and Trenton dry of fighting men. Once or twice, Mama said,
our heroine had shot a cannon herself, but more frequently she
succored the troops, bandaged the wounded, and faithfully carried water from the well that we visited so loyally.

"The pride, girls, oh, the pride you should have in your country. Pride in the gallantry, the bravery of our men," Mama declaimed.

"Nonsense," Papa interrupted. "Flag-waving patriotism is a poor thing."

"And what about you?" Mama replied. "What about all those endless Scottish gatherings?"

"Ceildhe," corrected Papa. "We have a ceildhe, not a gathering."

"Sometimes," Mama countered, "I think if I hear another bagpipe, I will go mad, raving mad."

"Piebrochs," said Papa.

"Well, they may be piebrochs to you, but they're bagpipes to me, and they make a fearful racket. And those children are more Scot then you are," said Mama, dismayed. "I can count their American friends on one hand."

"I can be both," I said with childish independence.

"Both what?" said Mama.

"Both Scottish and American; I can be both. I don't have to be just one or the other."

"Child, you're an American." And, glancing at Papa, she added, "I trust you will be a good one."

Our journey, then, to Molly's had special overtones for me. First, it was American. I supposed, naturally enough as a child, that if I drank enough water from her well, I would be a good American. Second, poor Papa was somehow in the wrong. I knew what he had done. He had never become a citizen. All those years, all those many years, and he could not do it.

"I could never do it," he once said to me conspiratorially.

"Don't think I didn't want to. Don't think it hasn't given me restless nights for many a year. I'm grateful to this country which has given me a home, a wife, my children," and then, patting my head, "my children's children. But oftentimes a man can't do it, lassie. He just can't say good-by to his country. The country that reared him, formed him, the country that was his world. He can't say good-by to it. Not forever."

"But you've never gone back," I said.

"I will, lassie, I will."

I tried to reconcile my two countries: the Scotland I had never seen, and the America that was all around me. It was not always easy. Sometimes I felt as much a stranger in my own country as Papa did on our excursions to the Well.

"Aye, it's your Scottish anarchy," said Papa. "Never be afraid, lassie, of rebellion in a good cause. Stand on your own two feet, girl. Sure of yourself, speak; and not sure, keep quiet until you learn. You'll learn, lassie. My mother had your fire."

"But I'm not all fire."

"Lassie, none of us are. We're fire and, mixed with the fire, ashes. Better a still flame, a still flame of rightness within us. Our own rightness. Remember that, child, remember that."

"Sometimes," I said almost to myself, "I want to be plain American, just plain American."

"Aye." Papa laughed. "It's the Mary Queen of Scots in you warring with the Molly Pitcher."

New Jersey is dotted with churches that saw the torment of the Revolution. Our excursion was always the same. My sister and I would sit in the back seat of the car with Mama. We would be restless with excitement and anticipation. At our feet would be the large picnic hamper. One summer we children sat on pillows. We had just been inoculated for the whooping cough that still racked us from time to time. But nothing could stay this trip. Aunt Fiona and Papa sat in the front seat. For once, in the excitement of driving together, they were friends. For the rest of the year, it seemed to me, they were enemies. Papa, when he was with Fiona, was all Scot; Fiona, always stubbornly American.

"Now, children," she would call out from the front seat, "the way to learn is to see. Keep your eyes open. We'll read the historical markers and stop when there's something interesting."

"I've got to go to the bathroom," Gogo whispered to me.

"Well, you'll just have to wait," I answered, sharing the same need. "You'll just have to wait until there's something interesting to see."

"Will it have a bathroom?" she asked anxiously.

"I don't know," I said. "You can never tell about churches."

The churches always came first. Mama had a special love for them; Fiona tolerated them; Papa avoided them. My sister and I didn't know what we felt.

"Can we have a sandwich?" I asked.

"Later. Later, when we get to Freehold."

Freehold had the most churches.

They were musty and damp and terribly silent. They were old and still and terribly cold.

"A fine way to spend a sunny day," Papa muttered. "What can the children learn this way?"

"They will learn," said Fiona, "how to be Americans."

"From what?" disputed Papa. "From blood on benches, touched up probably to give it a little authenticity? It's morbid, that's what it is."

"When do we get to Molly Pitcher's?" I asked, knowing full well it was the last stop but anxious to change the discussion.

"Later," said Mama. "Now don't be restless."

The famous well sat back from the road. Gogo and I always looked at each other in disappointment. It was so tiny. How could Molly Pitcher have watered a whole army? It was covered with flagstones and a raftered roof was erected above it. We raced each other to the spot and bent over the top. The inside of the well was cold, and we ran our hands down as far as we could reach. The moss was wet and tangled. The bucket hung above our heads, and attached to the rope was a tin cup.

"No, no," said Aunt Fiona as we reached for it. "Germs. Here's a paper cup."

Spring water needs the clashing taste of tin, but we capitulated. Each of us took a paper cup, and each drank a private toast.

"Do you feel differently?" my sister asked. "Really American?"

"Yes," I said. "I feel really American. And sometimes," I said to her in confidence, "I feel really Scot."

"Me, too," said Gogo.

Then, when no one was looking, we stole a drink from the tin cup. It was as fresh and heady as independence.

the old roots

Man, said Papa, as he looked at the country grass, needs roots. He needs them if only because he must trip in their twists and turns and sometimes fall full-face on the ground. It is important, said Papa, to fall just as it is important to stand up straight and look at the sky.

"Never forget that," he said. "It's the one important thing I can tell you. It's just as important to be thrown upon the earth as it is to stand tall and straight as a mountain and look into the heavens.

"For that reason," said Papa, "we need roots.

"For that reason, I have always been sad, heavy in my heart, for twice in my life I was uprooted. The first time was so long ago and far away that I can barely remember it."

As I sat there and listened to him, I could see his memories churn; I could see him struggle and, bewildered, seek out and try to find some root on which he could clasp a tendril of memory. Some stone by which he could guide himself. Some cairn of his fathers upon which he could rest his stone. Papa had always told me that Scots feel comfortable only when they build a cairn on the grave or the fallen spot of the ancient heroes.

"You will, I know, my lass," said Papa, "build a cairn for me in something you write or in the fresh lives of your children."

"You mean much more than stones, Papa," I said. He deserved far more. He deserved a whole mountain or a river or all the lochs of Scotland. My voice trembled when I tried to tell him everything he deserved and how much he meant to me.

"That is childhood," said Papa. "I am your grandfather and you're my grandchild. My memory and your memory are all mixed up in the way of generations. I have passed some color of my dreams on to you, and from you I get some of my breath and some of my blood to deal with tomorrow.

"Call your sister," he would say, "and I'll tell you about when I was a boy in Scotland . . ."

We had heard the story time and time again, but each time we eagerly drew closer and heard it once more. Each time in the way of our ancient Celtic shanachies, our storytellers, he would start in with the frills and rills of storytelling, and each time he would embroider and enlarge upon his tale.

"I was exiled twice," said Papa.

"What's exile?" said Gogo.

"It's hard to explain. It means that in some strange way you are cut off from the places that you've known; that you're cut off from the things that you have remembered. They are so far away that they are almost forgotten, in the way people are almost forgotten when you do not see them for a long time."

"Oh," said Gogo, "that's like a summer vacation. A summer vacation is an exile from all those people you see in the winter. And winter school is exile from all those people you see in the summer. Have you ever thought of that, Seon? Isn't that about the way it is?"

"That sounds right," I said. "Would you call that exile, Papa?"

"Not quite," said Papa. "But I can see that there's a little of exile in leaving and parting. A writer named Schopenhauer said that to part is a foretaste of dying."

"I hate dying things," said Gogo. "I hate people that die and I hate dying bugs, and I even hate a little dog when he dies."

"It happens," said Papa. "It happens."

And that was the way Papa explained his first exile. It had simply happened.

"I was five years old," said Papa. "You remember, girls, how it felt to be five years old?" I shook my head.

"I remember," said Gogo. "I can remember when I was five and I wanted so much to be six and I was very glad I wasn't four."

"You were a very mature little girl," said Papa. "Well, when I was five," he continued, "I was not so mature. I was a frightened little boy on a Scottish island."

"What island?" I asked Papa quickly.

"It does not matter," said Papa. "What matters is that when

I was five, my father and mother, with me, my brothers, and my sister Bride left our island and went to Glasga."

I listened to his voice as he was relating these familiar facts. I was just beginning to realize how life was made up of such blunt facts—how old you are, who your sisters and brothers are, when your father and mother left their island.

"We went to Glasga," said Papa. The way he said it had a fascination all its own. It sounded like Glasga, and years later I could always tell whether the speaker was from Glasgow by the truncated ending that he gave his town's name.

"When we came from the Islands to Glasga, it seemed I had never seen so many people in the whole wide world. If you multiplied the Biblical multitude over again, it still would not have seemed as crowded to me as were the streets of Glasga."

"That's because you were five," said Gogo. "I remember, Papa, that when I was five, everybody still seemed so big. They don't any more. I feel bigger, but everybody else doesn't seem so big."

"I think all the important ages go by fives," said Papa. "I felt it was the most important age in the world when I was five, and by the time I was ten . . . Oh, by the time I was ten, my father was dead. By the time I was fifteen, my mother was dead. By the time I was twenty, my brothers were dead."

"But not Bride," we said in unison. The tale was too sad. "Not Bride," we said.

"No," said Papa, "not Bride. Bride, God bless her, she will last."

Papa was right. Our Aunt Bride did live many years after his death, and on her death, she left us with a fine taste for the

63

rich country-Ireland that she called her foster home, as well as with a small legacy that allowed us later to go abroad and retrace our own heritage.

When she had left the isles of Scotland to go to Glasgow with her brothers and her parents, she was already fourteen. She was, said Papa, a girl of unusual intensity and somehow or other she became what is called, or what was called then, an Educated Girl.

There were few Educated Girls at that time, but long ago in Edinburgh there had been very many Educated Boys. These were young people who, like the tobacco readers in the old cigar factories, read to the assembled workers to amuse them as they worked.

You could call Aunt Bride a form of today's Muzak. She was an Educated Girl and she was hired as a reader in the factories in Glasgow. Bit by bit she made enough money to attend medical school in Edinburgh, where she was one of the first women to graduate from those august and, I thought, very, very scary halls—halls that had produced such terrible and ghastly stories as those eighteenth-century Burke and Hare murders, a bevy of stolen bodies and grave-snatchings that I could see at the Thalia movie house at the corner of Ninety-fifth Street.

Aunt Bride held a warm affection in my heart. I loved her most because she gave me the proper ammunition to use against my friend, Mary Finnegan, with her interminable talk about the old country.

"Aunt Bride," I said, "loves Ireland. She says it's as green and soft as the banks of the Shrewsbury River."

"Where's that?" said Mary Finnegan.

"In New Jersey," I said.

"I think," I said, "the name Bride is one of the loveliest names I've ever heard." I pronounced it, of course, as I had been taught—to rhyme with mead.

"Only pigs breed," said Mary Finnegan, "pigs and hogs. I think it's an awful name."

"Oh, you're quite wrong," I said. "Bride, you know, was the mother of all Ireland. Bride's a Gaelic name. Bridget is the way you say it in English."

"You're lying, Seon," said Mary. "I don't know why you lie so much. My mother's name is Bridget and she certainly wouldn't have any kind of hog-whining, noisy name like that."

I was struck down by the attack, and for a moment I was silent. Bride and need, I thought. What lovely words. Years later, when I thought of Joyce wandering about the streets of Dublin, hunting words, seeking sounds, and tripping occasionally over his own epiphanies, I reflected on how the words Bride and need had led me down so many paths of life and letters.

Bride was the mother of all Ireland. In Irish mythology, she was one of the triad of goddesses of day, light, and life, and over the years our Aunt Bride became less and less an individual and more and more a potent force; a fantasy of light, life, day; a goddess.

"She always seemed, even to me," said Papa, "like a goddess." She was much older and she was very, very bright. Bride means bright; bright and brilliant. And I guess if you have a name, you must live up to that name. Bride did. "Though I've never," Papa added, "seen how she could study medicine with all its blood and gore and all its pain and misery. I've never been able to see that at all. And yet sometimes I can, because I remember after we left the Islands, there in Glasga in the Gorbals the winters were as cold and miserable as any winters could be.

"The Gorbals were one of the ghastliest slums that any people have ever been forced to live in. And in those narrow, dirty streets, where the houses pushed one against the other like the white fever they sheltered, with people demanding their rights just to live and breathe, I knew that some would get out; some would leave that ghetto.

"Bride did," said Papa. "And I did. But some of the others had to leave by different doors. My parents," he said sadly, "left by those doors and would never return through any other door again. Then my brothers. The Gorbals were slums that claimed their share of the dead as much as any steerage ship later did.

"They talk about the steerage," said Papa, "but the truth is, there are all kinds of steerage and exile through life."

"And that," said Gogo, interrupting, "is when you came to Ellis Island. Isn't that so, Papa? And then you went down to the country and you met Mama, and then our mother was born and everything was all right again. Isn't that right?" said Gogo, anxious to break the sad threads of the story.

"Not quite as fast as that," said Papa, "not quite as fast as that. It seemed like a horror and a terrible waste of time from the moment I first thought of coming to the United States until the time I got here."

"What made you think of it, Papa?" I asked. "Was it something that grew in your heart like a great idea until finally it burst forth and forced you out of the Gorbals and into the wide, wide world?"

"I don't know," said Papa. "Well, yes, I do know. More than likely it was *Coming Through*."

"That's a part of the story I like," said Gogo. "*Coming Through* was the horse, wasn't he? The most wonderful horse in the world that you rode faster than the wind, and you were the greatest rider in the world, weren't you, Papa? And that's why you came to this country, and then you went down to Shrewsbury and you met Mama."

"Step by step," said Papa, "step by step."

In Papa's bedroom, there were several objects that never ceased to amaze us. Over the brass bedstead was a riding crop, beautifully carved at the tip in ivory. Above his bed there was an odd assortment of pictures and photographs and mementos that he had on the walls, as though in some way each one of these would hold him to the present or remember him to the past. There was a lithograph of a horse that was beautiful in every detail. On a rainy day, Gogo and I would sit crosslegged on the floor and look up at this wonderful, great beast that was surely a lord of all he surveyed. He had died many, many years ago, but he was one of the finest horses, Papa said, that ever lived, and through him, in some way or another, we knew Papa.

Feeling that he would be defeated by the Gorbals, Papa decided to abandon city life altogether and went down the coast of Scotland to the Robert Burns country and hired himself out as a groom. He was used to animals, and the horses instantly responded to his magnificent care of them.

His malnutrition had left him very light and small-boned, and as a result it was soon discovered that he made an excellent jockey. The laird of the manor decided to ship some of his horses to the United States, and over a period of two years Papa managed to manipulate the reins of destiny in such a way that eventually he, too—not as valuable as horseflesh but just as sensitive—was sent to the new world that lay across the sea.

"I can't tell you," said Papa, "how much it ached—the thought of putting Scotland behind me. When I put that behind me, I would put everything. I would put behind the memory of my brothers; the memory of my father and my mother; and the memory of the place—my islands and my moors. Yes, even of my horses, because only one, *Coming Through,* would be going with me. All that would be something I would never be able to retrace.

"Today it's so different. The boats go back and forth with such speed, and the time will come when you'll go in an airplane. You'll go so fast, you'll barely know you've left one place before you're in another. But it was different then. Even though it might not take more than two weeks to make a crossing, we knew we would never, in all likelihood, make it again."

"I guess it cost a million dollars," said Gogo. "Didn't it, Papa? Didn't it cost a million dollars just to get here?"

"It cost a million dollars of misery," said Papa, "but not too much money. People would be surprised really how very little

68

money it cost. I, of course, didn't have to pay anything because I accompanied *Coming Through,* and I was bedded down better in the stables aboard the boat than the people were. I never forgot that; the horses were important. Occasionally, I would eat a little hay that belonged to *Coming Through,*" he mused.

"When you were a boy," I said, "you'd eaten heather in the famine, wasn't that right, Papa?"

"And it's a ghastly cup of tea, I'll tell you that, lass. I wouldn't suggest a diet of heather for anybody; heather or green potatoes. The Irish, when they had them, would so frequently have green potatoes that they'd break out with sores and lumps. Still it was more digestible than heather. Heather is not good for anything except maybe a cup of heather tea and that, though it may warm your body for one fleeting moment, will send a chill through your marrow.

"Yes," said Papa, "we were hungry." He touched the warm cup of tea Mama had brought, and turned his words to her. "We were hungry sometimes for more than food. We were hungry for our homes; we were hungry for the future. Who were we, as we rode those waves? We could sink beneath them and who would care? Who was there to care? For some of us, there were people who were left. I thought of Bride so much during that trip. But for others there was no one. I had, too, *Coming Through.*

"I loved that horse," said Papa. "That whole voyage he seemed to make me stay alive deep down inside me. Somehow or other I had turned against people. People, at least the people on that trip, seemed so frightened; so terrified; so far different from ordinary people. They were people pressed.

"*Coming Through,* however, was doing just that. He was coming through the voyage, and he was coming through it with his head high and his hoofs clean and firm. He was coming through with a strong heart, and only his wind seemed to suffer from the lack of exercise, although I did my best to exercise him. I saddled him every day—saddled him and strapped him and mounted him. The stall and the dank smell of the ship are all mixed up in my mind and I'll never forget it.

"But with all the unhappiness there was a certain curious kind of joy, a kind of looking forward, a kind of coming through to a new excitement."

Gogo and I would draw closer then, as Papa's story reached the American shore. Papa had Come Through, and as we felt the twinges of growing up we knew, too, that we and our friends must complete the journey of being Americans. We must Come Through.

broom, green broom

Papa worked very, very hard at making our childhood easy; and he usually gave us the painful burden of being carefree. My sister and I were very suspicious of long summer days that stretched in front of us—days that somehow or other had to be filled with laughter and contentment, even if our spirits, or skins (because summer meant poison ivy to me), were rubbed harsh by childhood's many miseries. Papa had never had a summer.

"Why not, Papa?" I asked each summer. The question always arose on a Saturday morning as Papa dragged the lawn mower from its resting place. "Didn't you ever have a holiday when you were a boy?"

"Never a bit of it, never a bit of it, lass. Here, give me a hand pushing this machine off the porch."

We pushed and pulled and finally the machine would topple off the porch, falling on top of the pansy bed that huddled at the foot of the porch steps. I always thought that pansies looked a little silly, stupid even, and those pansies had a kind of moronic, blank expression that never changed despite the ill-treatment that my sister and I subjected them to. We walked upon them, trampled them, drenched them with buckets of water that we, like Poseidon's daughters, hurled from the porch.

"Careful of those pansies," said Papa. "You know how your grandmother feels about her flowers. I think I clipped one with the mower there. Pick it up like a good lass. Give it a heave over the fence."

"Not on Mrs. MacCallum's lawn," I answered in shocked disbelief. "We're never, never supposed to throw anything on Mrs. MacCallum's lawn. Not even a dandelion, Papa—not even a piece of clover."

"Oh, lassie, but you're the stubborn Scot. You've a regular John Knox conscience. What's the harm of a wee pansy?"

This difference of ethics between one generation and another always irritated him. The result was a sudden burst of speed with the mower, and in one smooth swath he had mowed down an iris, nicked a peony, and crushed a clump of chrysanthemums. I tried to distract Papa from the havoc he had caused, for guilt would hang heavy in his chest, I was sure.

"Just why didn't you have a summer, Papa?" I asked now, bending over and gathering the mower's mayhem, a miserable bouquet of wretchedness.

"No Scot has a summer," said Papa, somewhat relieved that the worst had occurred, and yet he had not hit a dahlia.

Mama's patience was remarkable. Silence, speechless rebuke were all that one received for harming pansies, mums, or iris; for the roses, there was a lengthy lecture; but for dahlias, there were tears. Mama had cried over many a dahlia, and it was a grief no one cared to subject her to.

"Is it against the law?" I asked.

"Is what against the law?" said Papa, who had sat down on the huge boulder where he rested from his labors at regular intervals.

"Are summers against the Scottish law?"

"Well, now, that's a weird question, that's a weird idea, lass. Where do you get some of those ideas?"

"Well, a lot of Scots do seem to be against a lot of things," I said aggressively.

"Aye, you've been having trouble with your aunt, I suppose. Well, no matter, I want you children to *enjoy* your summer."

"Because you never had one—right, Papa?" said my sister.

"I want you children to be carefree," said Papa, "to enjoy the grass and the flowers."

"And the birds," said Gogo.

"And the sky," I contributed.

"And dogs and cats, and lemonade, and the circus," said my sister.

"That's enough," Papa murmured. "Quiet down now. I want you to enjoy the summer. When I was a boy . . ."

The three of us settled on the rock and waited for Papa's memory and words to surge up into his heart, into his mouth, to spill over into a story. He hesitated a minute or two—and in those seconds I really felt carefree, I really enjoyed the whole world as though it were some ripe, rich gift that Papa had given us.

"When I was a boy every summer was as cold as winter."

"That's because you lived at the North Pole," my sister said.

"No, not at the North Pole," Papa said patiently, "but far north in the Islands. When I was a small laddie, I went to sleep with the sunlight in my face, though it could be well on to midnight."

"They let you stay up late," said my sister. "Will we ever stay up to midnight, Seon, ever?"

"I guess so," I said. "Go pick pansies, Gogo. Mama will like it if you pick pansies. Papa and I have things to talk about."

"*You* go pick pansies," said my sister. "You go pick your nose for all I care."

My attention wavered from Papa for a moment. My sister never ceased to amaze me. She talked just like poetry sometimes. I started to fool around with the raw stuff of her genius, and recited:

Whoever goes
To pick her nose,
Must touch her toes
Before she goes.

"That's poetry, Papa," I said. "How do you like that poem?"

Papa's thoughts were far away. "In the summer," he said, "we all cut broom."

My sister sang:

There's a broom
In the moon . . .

"Oh, shut up," I said. "Papa's talking."

"What's broom?" asked my sister, ignoring me completely.

"Did I never sing you the song about broom, lassies?"

"I just sang a song about broom," Gogo interrupted. "Didn't you hear it?"

"Don't be silly, Gogo. That's just a nonsense song," I explained. "Papa means a real song like 'cockles and mussels, alive, alive ho.'"

"Dead ho, dead ho," sang my sister. I didn't attempt to quiet her. Her shoulders were getting all red and she'd have a fierce sunburn. That would teach her.

"In Scotland they have fields of broom, don't they, Papa? Acres and hills and fields of it. Isn't that right, Papa?"

It was hard to rouse Papa when he got that look in his eyes. That faraway look that meant an ocean separated us. In sudden loneliness, I put my arm around my sister's shoulder.

"Ouch, that hurts. I'm hot."

"You'll get sunstroke, Gogo," I said kindly. "Maybe I should spit on your shoulders and take the sting out."

"What's this about spit?" said Papa. "You children should be playing. Go on your swings. Be carefree. You'll only have summer when you're children."

I didn't attempt to figure out that wistful illogic, but persisted in my efforts to get Papa to sing the broom song.

"Is it about witches on brooms, Papa?" I said, watching some birds circle in the sky. "Is it about cleaning the house

with brooms? Are they the same brooms or different brooms?
Sing it, Papa, please."

There was an old man and he lived in a wood,
And his trade it was making of broom, of broom.

"Papa's old," my sister whispered to me.
"Shsh," I said.

And he had a naughty boy, Jack, to his son
And he in bed till 'twas noon, 'twas noon.

"Is Uncle Jamie a naughty boy?" Gogo whispered.
"I don't know. Maybe. He does sleep to noon. But this is a
pretend song. Now listen."

Papa now struck a familiar pose. One foot rested on the
rock, his shoulders were straightened up, and his head was
thrown back, as a trickle of perspiration worked its way slowly
down his face. Just like a bug, I thought, a slow, lazy bug, and
I sat entranced, watching it crawl off his chin, while gloriously
unconcerned he sang on:

The father was vext and sorely perplext,
With passion he enters the room, the room,
"Come, sirrah," he cried, "I'll leather your hide
If you will not go gather green broom, green broom,
If you will not go gather green broom."

"Does Mama have a green broom?" Gogo said. "I think I'll
go ask her. I'm hot."

77

I was hot, too, but Papa had a look of real inspiration on his face and I didn't want to interrupt. I wished I had a lemonade. I was so distracted that I missed most of the words in the next verse, all except the refrain:

Pretty maids, do you want any broom, green broom?
Pretty maids, do you want any broom, green broom?

I liked that line and hummed it to myself over and over again while Papa sang to the birds and the flowers:

A lady looked out of her lattice so high
And spied Jack a-selling of broom, green broom,
Says she, "You young blade, won't you give up your trade
And marry a maid in full bloom, full bloom?"

Full bloom. The garden was in full bloom, now. I began to kick at the soil at my feet. Really, Papa's songs were too long. I always got lost listening to them. I wished Mama would bring a lemonade.

So they sent for the parson without much delay
And married they were in the room, the room.

Papa could go on forever at this rate, I knew. I began to pluck off the tops of the weeds.

There was eating and drinking, and Jack said with a wink,
"This is better than cutting of broom, green broom,
This is better than cutting of broom."

"Joseph!"

"Yes, dear," Papa greeted Mama. "The lawn's nearly finished."

"That's no song to be singing to the children, Joseph. I don't know what comes over you at times. You let the little one burn her shoulders, and you fill Seon's head with more words and nonsense than any child was meant to hear."

"But it was a nice song, Mama," I said. "It was better than cutting of grass, of grass," I said with sudden inspiration.

"You see, Joseph, it just encourages the children to be fresh."

"It was just a song," said Papa defensively. "I heard it myself when I was just a wee lad. It's kind of a summer song. You know, my dear, it kind of brings back the spring to me—with all the hills covered with tight yellow broom blossoms and the shrub itself all green and thorny."

"You didn't hit any roses with that machine, did you, Joseph?"

"No, never a rose." He drank the lemonade in one swift gulp.

"Well, my lassie," he said to me, his face quite different now, quite here and now, quite my Papa again. "Shall we be cutting the grass, green grass?"

I was filled with happiness. When I saw Mama disappear around the house, I gathered up Papa's garden havoc that I had hidden under the giant hydrangea bush, and with carefree abandon, threw it over the fence.

shakespeare the scot

It was inevitable that sooner or later our Sunday School would give a performance of *Macbeth*. We were not the type to don gay raiment and frisk and frolic through the lines of *A Midsummer Night's Dream*. There was, said Mrs. MacDonald, something indecent about *that* play. Definitely pagan—in any case not Presbyterian.

But *Macbeth*. That *was* Presbyterian. You could hear Calvin muttering along with those witches on the heath; you could hear the Scottish wind howling through the church basement. Besides, hadn't Miss Macbeth taught us all our letters in first grade? And besides, said Mr. Guthrie, wasn't the immortal Shakespeare himself a Scot? It was our birthright to perform his play.

"MacShake, the fake," muttered Johnny MacDonald to me, as we sat entranced by Mr. Guthrie, who was going to direct and be prompter for the play.

James Guthrie's ancestor had written a piece of exegesis that proved Shakespeare was a Highland chieftain with a fine braw of words, and it was only a piece of chicanery about that swan of Avon business. The British were always eager to get the Scottish tourist business, and what better way than to appropriate Shakespeare? He was not the swan of Avon—but the eagle of Ben Nevis. Therefore, it was appropriate that the spirit of the eagle of Ben Nevis should alight in the church basement, and, said Papa, when he heard the background of our projected performance, lay a royal Scottish egg.

Mrs. MacDonald, the Artistic Director, commanded us to gather all the discarded Christmas trees in the neighborhood. When Great Birnam wood to High Dunsinane should come, our Christmas trees would transform the heath that was our church basement.

Mrs. MacDonald also had some strange ideas about costumes. We should, she said, use our marks of distinction.

The boys and girls looked at each other with some embarrassment. This seemed a rather curious thing to say, and as we were all in an age trembling with adolescence, we were a little shy and very much aware of our badges of distinction.

"Look them up in your family history," she said.

That comment made it clear to us that it was the Scottish facts of life that interested Mrs. MacDonald, and, relieved, we sought advice.

"A mark of distinction," said Papa, "can be a tuft of heather or pine. We used to stick them in our bonnets. The MacDonalds, for example," said Papa, "wore a tuft of heather."

I could see Mrs. MacDonald in my mind's eye parading to

church on Easter with tufts and tufts of heather stuck in some elaborate hairdo.

"The MacGregors and the Grants too, for that matter, always wore a bunch of pine. The Drummonds and MacKenzies always wore the holly, but you have to be quite sure that the Drummonds wear the plain holly and the MacKenzies the variegated holly. The MacIntyres," continued Papa, "when they could get it, wore the boxwood, and the Stewarts—well, the Stewarts, always having to be different about one thing or another, wore the oak.

"Our badge," added Papa, with unabashed delight, "is also the holly." He went on with great pride, "And we can wear either the plain or the variegated."

This green litany gave Mama the hives, she said, but as long as no one had to wear poison sumac, she wished us luck.

Our performance of *Macbeth* was obviously to bring together all the members of our colony, old and young, just as it was the occasion in some way to celebrate not only present talent, of which there was little enough, but also past greatness. It was these ventures in which our parents and grandparents took some particularly overdeveloped way to explore past greatness that most distressed the young people.

Once again the church basement was wildly decorated with tartans, with swords (they seemed very appropriate at this point), with a few silver cups won by some of us in athletic contests with less aggressive schools, with the abandoned Christmas trees, and with a large area of sand. This sand was supposed to symbolize the heath, and it was Mrs. MacDonald's idea that the three witches could stand around, or rather kneel,

in this sand and let it trickle through their fingers as they repeated their never-to-be-forgotten lines. For good measure,
they were also to stand over a can of Campbell's soup in
Mama's iron pot.

I say, never-to-be-forgotten lines, because, naturally, as all
lines must be when they are repeated by a cast ranging from
eleven to fifteen years, they were more frequently forgotten
than not.

When shall we three meet again,
In thunder, lightning, or in, in, in . . .

" 'Rain,' " shouted Mr. Guthrie, our prompter. " 'In rain.' "

Fair is foul, and foul is fair:
Hover through the fog and filthy, and filthy, and
   filthy . . .

" 'Air,' " shouted Mr. Guthrie.

During these long rehearsals, we thought that was a most
appropriate line; the church basement was certainly filled with
fog and filthy air. For some reason, the odor of a gymnasium
hung about it—black stockings, sneakers, perspiration, exercise, exhaustion, competition, the strivings of adolescence to
grow to adulthood.

In the school gym, our bodies went through calculated
movements every day to attain some semblance of maturity.
Here now, as we rehearsed the ancient lines of *Macbeth*, some
part of our minds was trying the same deliberate exercise to

reach maturity. In this ancient play we seemed to try to come together with our own people. But, as always, our people's history seemed to be unabashedly bloody.

Lady Macbeth, for example. Why was it, we asked each other, that the witches were more effective than Lady Macbeth? The truth was, Mr. Guthrie had a great deal of difficulty even finding anybody willing to accept that very rich role. He finally settled on Mary Boswell.

The selection of Mary Boswell seemed unfortunate. She was shorter than the rest of us and had golden hair. This in itself seemed quite strange because, as a whole, there were not too many fair-haired children in the school. Mary was one of the gentlest of all girls, and it did not seem quite possible to imagine any of the bloody deeds or restless words of the play in connection with her. We were startled then when we heard one of those fabulous lines echo from her mouth and bounce around the corners of the gymnasium.

" 'Leave all the rest to me.' "

Mr. Guthrie obviously knew what he was doing, and he left most of her lines to Mary Boswell without urging her in any practice or rehearsal sessions. Mary, for her part, spent most of her time trying to find something suitable to wear. We children decided to do a little research of our own and felt that we would come up with some very exciting ideas.

Mrs. MacDonald had given us the hint; after the wild search (and it had been unsuccessful) for the badges in which we should all represent our clans, she abandoned her efforts toward ancient authenticity. By that time, however, we had captured an ancient enthusiasm as fearsome as the wind on Macbeth's heath.

We went to the library and managed to get an entire series of books on Scottish heraldry. We turned to a majestic volume called *Scottish Heraldry Made Easy* and decided that within those pages might be all the details we would need for a really effective performance of *Macbeth*. It never occurred to us, of course, that learning the lines might be the most effective way to present any play.

The list of principal Scottish crests supplied us with a fascinating pile of misinformation. From the name Adam (surely it was a point in favor of a Scottish heritage that our genealogy stretched back to Adam) to that blessed Wallace for whom most Scots had bled to the wonder that there were any of us left at all, all the Septs and Clans rode the pages in glorious array.

"The thing to do," said Mary, "is to find out what crest belonged to Macbeth."

"Papa told me," I said, "and it wasn't very much."

"Well, then, we'll just have to make believe," said Mary.

This was a new side of Mary, and I listened to her with new respect. She had always seemed to me a remarkably unimaginative girl, far too golden and glistening, and really quite dull for all her sunshine.

"If we don't use Macbeth," Mary said, "we'll use MacBain."

"What do you mean?" asked Johnny MacDonald.

"Why, look, we'll use the crest of MacBain that comes right before Macbeth, and it's a better one anyway."

"They'll know the difference," said Johnny disgustedly.

"The MacLean crest was a tower," I remarked.

"And furthermore," said Johnny, in even greater disgust, "you'll never be able to fool them."

"I have no desire to fool them," said Mary. "I've only got an interest in making this whole performance more dramatic."

We were silent in admiration. Imagine Mary figuring out that there might be some possible way in which we could make the performance really dramatic.

"The MacBain crest," said Mary, "has a cat salient."

"What does that mean?" Johnny asked. "A cat salient?"

"I don't know," said Mary. "What do you suppose it is, Seon? Do you know?"

"I think it's leaping," I said. "I think that's what salient means—leaping."

"A leaping cat." Mary sucked in her breath. "That's what I'll do. Just imagine, I'll give the whole performance," said our Lady Macbeth, "with a cat on my arm."

The sheer imaginative glory of it struck us quite dumb, and yet, could it be done?

"Do you think Mr. Guthrie would approve?" I said. "I don't think there really is a cat in *Macbeth*."

"It doesn't matter," said Mary, now quite sure of herself. "I know this is what we should do and I know we should have a cat. We don't have a cat. Do you have one, Johnny?"

"No."

"Do you, Seon?"

"No," I said, "but we could use Major."

Major. Major was the finest cat in our neighborhood. He
was the church cat or, as Papa would often say, the true Presbyterian cat, the true Seceder Cat of the old poem. But Major
looked gay and abandoned, fat and far too well fed, far too
well indulged for any true Presbyterian. He did have a look
about him, though, of intense seriousness, intense dedication,
and he was, of course, dedicated to the church as the church
was to him. He roamed all week long through the lower
reaches of the church house, through the basement, through
the washrooms. As a matter of fact, the only water he ever
drank was from the toilet bowls and, although water was put
out to him with fair regularity, the skill with which he strad-
dled the toilet bowl to drink that water was really startling to
us all.

"The thing about Major," said Mary, "is he will understand.
If ever I've seen a cat that looked like a true Macbeth cat,
Major is that cat. Wouldn't you say so, Johnny?"

Johnny scratched his head.

"Well, we're using our imagination, anyway, Johnny," I
said. "After all, look at all of Mrs. MacDonald's hollies and
grasses and yews. I've got the yew line, did you know that,
Johnny? 'Gall of goat and slips of yew, silvered in the moon's
eclipse.' "

"That's not important," said Mary aggressively. "What's
really important is Lady Macbeth. Lady Macbeth is the most
important person in the play."

Neither Johnny nor I answered. It was quite true that, even
though he was playing Macbeth, it was obvious to all of us

that Lady Macbeth was the most important person in the play and that Mary Boswell was quite the most important person, at least for a brief while, on our street.

It didn't seem wise to rehearse with Major. All the young people, who were now intensely interested in the performance because of the addition of the new player, decided that we would keep this great piece of theatrical imagination for the night of the performance. That night, fortunately, came before the last of the Christmas tree needles dropped from the branches, for they made the floor of the basement slippery and treacherous for a year afterward.

We got off to the rousing start that the opening of *Macbeth* allows everyone. The thunder and lightning were distantly supplied by the church organist, and we boiled and bubbled into that ancient ritual play. Despite the fact that my contribution to the performance in the person of the third witch was quite negligible, my excitement continued to increase throughout the evening, because it was not until Act Five that we had decided it would be important for Major to make his grand and noble entrance. The stage directions read, "Enter Lady Macbeth with a taper." To those who were more familiar with the play than we were, perhaps the difference in the way that Lady Macbeth entered was even more striking than it seemed to us, and to us it seemed overwhelming.

Mary Boswell was wearing a long, white, flannel nightgown. It must have been her grandmother's, and it fell quite whimsically from one shoulder. The other shoulder was wrapped around and around with the plaid of a Cameron; her mother was a Cameron and this matriarchal touch was obvious and familiar to all of us. The tartan was a bit too long and she tripped over it at fair intervals. But the major piece of theatricality sat on her arm, or rather climbed on her arm. Major, frightened by the theater lights, had dug his claws into her shoulder, and Mary's face, now fatigued by the long performance, was strained and white.

"Look at her," whispered Johnny MacDonald, briefly offstage. "Wouldn't she give you the willies? Doesn't she look like Lady Macbeth herself?"

The closeness of the basement was beginning to affect us all. The witchcraft of Shakespeare's *Macbeth* had clawed at the audience. Sometimes it resulted in just a scratch on its sense of humor, but sometimes it went deeper and rich, wild language rang out.

In that great scene, Lady Macbeth's sleepwalking scene, Major gave Mary a long gash. When she looked down and said, "Oh, oh, oh"—putting her oh, oh, oh's in the wrong place —"Oh, oh, oh, out damned spot, out I say," she tried to throw Major away from her. Major would not give.

We players stood silently, held by the drama. This was a greater force than we had imagined. Not Lady Macbeth trying to cope with her evils and sins, but Mary simply trying to cope with a frightened Major.

" 'Out, damned spot, out, I say,' " cried Mary.

Always an effective line, it was even more effective now because there was a drop of blood on Mary's skin where Major had clawed her. She was equal to this dramatic moment and even more equal to a great Shakespearean line that she threw to the winds.

91

"Out, salient cat," she said. "Out!" And with all her might and main, she threw Major from her shoulder.

The line drew the greatest applause of the evening, and somehow or other the rest of the characters fumbled and fought their way to the end.

But the great and final ending was yet to come. In this Mary was no longer important. All were dead—Lady Macbeth, Macbeth. Now for the final dramatic moment that we young people had worked out together.

MacDuff, in the person of Duncan Farson, entered. He carried the long silver tray that belonged to Mama, a tray which came out only at Christmas time and which we had special permission to use for this one evening only. The tray was covered with a scarf and under that scarf we knew what wickedness lay: it was Macbeth's head.

Of course, we were quite incapable of producing Macbeth's head, but we had done, we thought, Shakespeare once again one better. We all shouted in chorus the one mighty line, " 'Hail, King of Scotland.' " MacDuff pulled aside the scarf and while the audience gasped, we hoped, for breath, Major, frightened, driven with excitement, leaped from the tray.

Papa said it was the most original performance of *Macbeth* he had ever seen. Mrs. MacDonald said it would all have been much better if we had only had some real yews. Mr. Guthrie said it was far too difficult for the young people really to understand what it was all about, and Mama said Major had scratched her tray.

It was interesting, however, that Mr. Guthrie never mentioned again how Shakespeare was Scottish and that it was our birthright to perform him. As a matter of fact, his only comment on our performance was that we were entirely too inspired.

the flavor of history

Washington's Birthday was nearly always a radiant day. At teatime we traditionally had a guest—Mrs. Farrell. There would be a cake in the shape of a log, chocolate hatchets for Gogo and me, and Papa's best tea. Darjeeling it was—it bubbled out its name in the cup. What a glorious name, I thought. And rivaled only by Margaret Riordan Connelly Farrell.

Mrs. Farrell fascinated us. She was a woman of mystery. Did she or did she not wear a wig? Even Mama and Papa were not sure, and, although they were always careful to avoid discussing the possibility in the presence of *the children,* we children sensed the excitement of their wonder. Something Mama and Papa did not know was extraordinary in itself, but somehow or other a wig, otherwise outside all our experience, was like some great nest mothering all manner of fantasies.

"It could cook her brains," said Gogo. "Golly, Seon, she

must be awful, awful hot. Do you think birds live in there?"

"You'd hear birds chirp," I said wisely. "But I agree that she must get hot. There's so much hair."

"We could ask her," said Gogo.

"Whether she's hot?"

"No, whether it's a wig. She wouldn't dare tell a lie on Washington's Birthday. What would happen, Seon, if you told a lie on Washington's Birthday?"

"They'd probably take a hatchet, Washington's hatchet, and chop your head off."

"They wouldn't, would they, Seon? Who'd do it? The President?"

"Probably," I said. Hoover didn't look like an executioner, but there had been a picture of Hoover with a Christmas turkey in the newspapers, and there had been pictures of hatchets and turkeys in the Sunday supplements.

"Probably right on the White House lawn. Like in France," I said, giving my imagination a walk into the French Revolution. "Just like in *A Tale of Two Cities*. You know, right on the White House lawn where the children roll Easter eggs. That would be a good place."

I paused reflectively. Mrs. Farrell was an aristocrat. Papa said you could see it in the way she stood. Only peasants stoop, Aunt Fiona told us often. Stand up—stand up straight.

I straightened my shoulders, and my chest tightened. Suddenly I felt frightened for Mrs. Farrell. There was going to be a revolution. Papa said so. It was about time, said Papa. Just watch the next election. The people will express themselves. Don't forget that march on Washington.

I could see another march on Washington—thousands of people, all the people who lived in the miserable shacks across the Hudson on the foul-smelling marshes amid the soot of burning rubbish and refuse. The sky was stained with smoke from the small fires that would explode into Papa's revolution. Maybe they'd take Mrs. Farrell, carry or push her all the way to Washington, and pelt her with Depression apples, but, I sighed with relief, that was *all.*

Mrs. Farrell was an aristocrat, but that was long ago, in another country, Papa said.

"Maybe she's got treasure hidden in her hair," said Gogo, "or secret documents."

"Perhaps," I agreed. It made sense. That was where aristocrats hid their jewels. Or spies their papers. Particularly if they had hair that wound around and around like a burnished copper crown.

That, said Aunt Fiona, she *could* tell about. It was dyed hair, as sure as sure could be.

But it was glorious, I thought. It must surely reach her toes. Maybe she tripped on it getting into bed.

"Long ago," I told Gogo, "she must have been an Irish queen. Queen Maeve," I said dramatically. "Queen of the Underworld."

"With gangsters," said Gogo, precociously involved in the gunplay of the time.

"No, stupid—the real underworld. Where there are leprechauns and fairies, and . . ."

"Mama says that's Papa's nonsense."

"Mama doesn't know," I said. "Mama doesn't know everything."

"Mrs. Farrell's got the biggest bosoms in the world," said Gogo. "Doesn't she, Seon? Do you suppose she's got jewels hidden between her bosoms?"

"Just hankies," I said. "Did you ever watch? She can pull out one hanky after another. And they all smell differently. It's like a whole garden of flowers. She must have a *million* hankies in her bosom."

"She must be rich," said Gogo. "I hope she buys Depression apples. Millions of them."

"She means well," I said graciously, imitating Mama's inflection and patience with the rich. Mama's infinite tolerance was strained by the idea of too much wealth, too much height (Mrs. Farrell smiled down at us from six feet), and too much hair.

Mrs. Farrell was Irish, and no one ever mentioned or even wondered about Mr. Farrell. That was fitting, I thought, because with the Irish queens, Maeve and Bride, husbands were not important. If Irish Queens had babies, I had reasoned long ago, they were like the ancient Greeks, and the babies came from the wind or the sea, or a river, or, as I looked at Mrs. Farrell carefully, the sun. The sun would surely be enamored of that hair. I studied her carefully as she sat in the corner chair by the window. In the right light the sunbeams cavorted in dust and dance, and I wanted to see if any sought her out. "The children of her bosom," I thought romantically.

"Pass the sandwiches, Seon," said Mama, reminding me by

her tone that the children of her bosom buttered the bread and passed the cake *before* helping themselves.

Oh, to be a sunbeam, I dreamed.

"You skipped me," said Gogo.

Mrs. Farrell ate like a queen. One cup of tea; one petit four.

The gluttony of commoners overcame me, and I snatched another cookie.

Now Mrs. Farrell took out her long cigarette holder, tapped it against the oak library table.

(If she were really a fairy queen, the oak would have moaned out, cried a lament. That oak table could be an Irish prince held in some spell. If she were a spy, it might be some secret message.)

"Fetch more milk, Seon."

I rushed to and from the kitchen, anxious not to miss Mrs. Farrell's smoking.

Mrs. Farrell inhaled, sighed, coughed ever so gently, contemplated the room through a vapor of exhaled smoke, and then regally, majestically let the ash fall on her capacious bosom.

"Let me give you a receptacle," said Papa gallantly.

Mrs. Farrell waved his offer aside.

"You can best help," said our lady reflectively, "by doing your bit for the Celts."

"The Lord helps those . . ." said Papa.

"Who help themselves," Gogo finished for him. "Can I have more cake?"

"Scotland is slow to burn," said Mrs. Farrell.

Not Mrs. Farrell. But she'll burn up someday, I thought, as

I watched another ash fire the skin of her décolletage, spit like a sunbeam, and disappear.

"The Irish cannot do it all," said Mrs. Farrell.

"Just what do you propose, Margaret?" Papa asked.

"I'd like to see you more active in the Pan-Celtic movement."

"Foolishness," said Papa. "What do you propose I do? Folk dancing?"

Mrs. Farrell ignored his remark—and him. She ignored all of us as she smoked her way into history. Mrs. Farrell was history.

She had seen civil war. Not, Papa explained, the war of Lincoln and Grant. She had sat on Parnell's lap. As a child, Papa had rushed to explain. And who was Parnell? I guess you could call him the father of his country. Like Washington. "Some Washington," disputed Mama.

"We Celts have a noble history," said Mrs. Farrell now.

She lit another cigarette, and let the ashes fall. She flicked the dust from her bosom with one hand, spilled a cup of tea in her lap—yet was above it all, beyond it all.

I was amazed. Even discomfort could not affect a queen.

It was evening by the time Mrs. Farrell gathered her belongings together—the great black coat that whipped her ankles, the capacious purse that held cigarettes, hairpins, clippings from the Irish press, a bundle of letters from Yeats and Lady Gregory. When she had been one of the most active women in the Irish Civil War, this great ripe soul had suffered and, now, must suffer in the subway.

A queen, I thought, should not travel by subway. Did people know that when Mrs. Farrell swayed in a subway car, history was passing by?

"If Parnell was the father of his country, did he wear a white wig like Washington?" asked Gogo. "Did he ever tell a lie? Was Mrs. Farrell the mother of her country?"

"Come on," I said when we were in bed and the lights were out. "Let's eat our chocolate hatchets. I put them under our pillows."

History has many flavors.

"let us be like bluebirds"

The Scots, said Papa, had invented modern banks.

Perhaps that was the reason why the Bank Holiday of the Depression came with such an enormous shock to our group of friends.

"I'll never get to *King Kong* now," said Johnny MacDonald mournfully. "The greatest movie in the world, with the most glorious monster that has ever been, and I'll never get to see it. Even in Loch Ness there was never a monster like that. Imagine, Seon, climbing up the side of the Empire State Building, just hanging on by your fingernails; doesn't it give you the shudders to think about it?"

I looked at my fingernails carefully. Johnny and I were growing apart. We were at that delicate age when we would begin to turn toward our own sex to clothe the fact that we were perhaps too much interested in the other sex.

"It's silly," I answered somewhat belligerently. "I would never want to hurt my fingernails by climbing up some silly old building. Besides, you couldn't do it, anyway. Besides, there isn't any such thing as a King Kong."

"You're no fun any more," said Johnny. "I might as well go play with Duncan. I'm not coming over again, not even in the rain."

"Well," I said hesitantly, sad to lose him because he was my dearest friend, "we could still walk to school together, I guess."

"No," said Johnny, "I don't think we should even be seen together on the streets. We're different, that's all. Different. You'll never know what it feels like to want to see *King Kong* —maybe even be him."

"And you," I said, "will never know how to keep your fingernails clean."

Then I began to sing, " 'Let us all be like bluebirds,' " and Johnny joined in.

" 'Happy all day long, forgetting all our troubles in a sunny song.' "

"That's a silly song," said Johnny.

"That's Mr. Woodin's song," I said. "Mr. Woodin is going to be in Washington. He's going to be the Treasurer. He made that song up."

"I bet he's never played the bagpipes," said Johnny.

"Well, neither have you," I said. "Even though you're a showoff."

He struck out and almost hit me. "You're a mean girl," he said. "My father told me this is the time we should all stick together. He says it's going to be awful; says it's going to be like the famine was in Scotland. People will be hungry and there wouldn't even be any heather to eat."

"Maybe there won't be any tripe either," I said. "I hate tripe —especially creamed tripe. I think tripe is worse than King Kong even. Johnny," I added, with a sudden, imaginative, culinary grasp of life, "tripe is nothing but the gizzard of some giant King Kong. It's a devil's meal, surely enough."

"We'll be hungry," said Johnny, not paying any attention to me. "Maybe we'll be thirsty too, and there won't be any tea. I suppose we'll all be dead before long. Maybe we'll never grow up. Wouldn't you think, Seon," he went on, "here I am a boy who may never grow up—wouldn't you think my Da would be generous enough to at least give me money to see *King Kong?*"

"That's fair," I said. "Maybe Papa would treat us. Papa says Mr. Roosevelt will make things better."

" 'Let us be like bluebirds,' " sang Johnny. "Maybe it's not such a bad song after all. Say, I have a good idea. Do you think I could get Mr. Roosevelt to lend me the money to see *King Kong?*"

"I expect he's busy," I said. "Otherwise I bet he would. That's the kind of man he is, Papa says."

"We'd better get what's coming to us now," said Johnny. "That's what my Da thinks. In the long run," Johnny went on, "there's nobody you can trust, except your own clan, and even then, says my Da, he wouldn't trust them too often. When I grow up, and I'm a writer and publish great stories like *King Kong,* people will want to know me. I'll be like Roosevelt and

I'll have my picture in the papers. Who, by the way," Johnny asked, "are John Doe and Jane Doe?"

"Papa says they're pretend names," I answered.

"They don't look pretend," said Johnny. "They look real." And as we sat there at the table, we looked at the pictures in an ad together.

John Doe and Jane Doe at a local bank. By three o'clock that afternoon, that bank had closed its doors with milling crowds of people outside still crying, shouting, demanding their money.

"I could see it coming," Mr. Ferguson told Papa. "Sure as my name is Ferguson, I could see it coming. Any Presbyter in the nation must have known it. Half of the collections have been I. O. U.'s for the last two weeks. You must know it yourself, Joe? It's been maybe longer coming, but it's here to stay. When the bank goes, everything goes. It's a betrayal."

My sister and I determined we would not be betrayed. Between us we had secreted, in various hiding places throughout the house over the past year, about two dollars in small change. Each one of us hid the other one's money, and in that way, when we came across it unawares, rustling through the China closet, or behind the books in the big bookcase, or inside the ceramic chicken that Mama used to serve rice, it was a glorious discovery. Now with careful determination we decided to round up our worldly wealth. At the same time that we did so, we were very frightened by a story that Johnny MacDonald told us. There was a boy in Illinois, he said, who saved 11,357 pennies toward his college education. They surrounded his home and they were trying to get all that money away from the boy.

"If," said Johnny, "you've got any money at all, you girls better give it to me. I'll keep it."

"I wouldn't trust you, Johnny," said Gogo. "I think it's safer just where it is."

"How would you know?" said Johnny. "You don't know what's safe. I remember when you were little and you wanted to keep your ice-cream cone after everybody had had theirs, you just hid yours somewhere, and when you went back to get it, it was all melted. You don't think, Gogo. If you hide that money now and you don't know where it is, it'll just melt. All its value will just melt right away."

Gogo and I listened to him seriously. Johnny appeared to have the makings of a banker.

"Now listen to my proposition," said Johnny. "I'll take your money and I'll give you my personal I.O.U. We'll lend all our change to other people for fifty percent more. If someone asks us for a nickel, they're going to have to give us seven-and-a-half cents back. They don't have to give it back to us fast, but they'll have to give us an I. O. U. right away. And I bet later, when things are better and Mr. Roosevelt really gets into operation, we'll have a fortune."

"Well, I don't know," said Gogo hesitantly.

"You've got to think fast," said Johnny. "You're not the only girls with two dollars, you know."

"Well, I don't really know if I can trust you," said Gogo.

"A MacDonald?" said Johnny.

Gogo said no more. She gave Johnny our collection of small change, but she seemed regretful about it.

Johnny told us, almost with tears in his voice, a month later, that he had taken the two dollars and gone to see *King Kong* down at Radio City.

"And the awful thing," he said, "the awful thing about it was that I was so scared, and there was nobody else there—the theater was like a great big, empty tomb."

"It serves you right," said Gogo, and held out her hand. Even as a little girl, she was a true Scottish banker. Over a year he paid her back the two dollars and a dollar in interest.

the words of saturday night

Saturday night was the last chance. Every Scot knew that. There was no point in pretending that you could have fun on Sunday. Even Sunday dinner would be as heavy as dumplings, and the quality of the day, if a quality could be captured, was like a floury dumpling: sticky, heavy, and choking—you were bound to choke at least once on Sunday's chicken bones, cough once over Sunday's dumplings, and cry once deep inside you for Sunday's misery.

Saturday night was the last chance.

Every Scot appreciated it; every Scot used it a different way. Mama, who was no Scot, nonetheless signaled the start of Saturday night. Instead of supper, we had high tea.

"A silly name for supper," Mama said.

"A grand time for talk," said Papa. "A breather from work."

"What's it like to go to work, Papa?" I asked.

"The first day of it, lass," said Papa, "sends your soul straight dead. The Irish have an expression, you know, 'He had my heart scalded,' and I don't think there's any one of us who hasn't looked upon his first employer as a man depriving him of life, liberty, and the pursuit of happiness."

"Why do people have to work?"

"I suppose," said Papa, "it's got something to do with the Garden of Eden."

"What nonsense is that, Joe?" said Mama, calling from the kitchen.

"I know my Bible," said Papa. "Of course, the other Scots bible is Samuel Smiles, the Self-Help man. In Samuel Smiles lived one of the greatest men of the nineteenth century."

"Like Parnell," I said.

"Great heavens," said Papa, "not a thing to do with Parnell. Smiles was a city man. We've always labored in Scotland, but in the islands when I was a boy, people worked as hard as animals, and yet they changed their labor and gave it variety and they gave it song.

"I can remember my mother," said Papa, "when I was such a wee bairn, spinning and singing the strangest of all songs. An old, old spinning song. There'd be the rhythm of the spinning and then a long pause and then the music and then the rhythm again. And as my mother would roll and card her wool, the verse and chorus would all go together to that spinning and singing, and the wheel, the fastness and the slowness and the sound of the bobbin, would all be one and the same. You'd be interested in this, Bertha. All the different kinds of songs there were. There were the heating songs."

"To be sung, I suppose," said Mama, "standing over a hot stove."

"No, lass," said Papa, "as a matter of fact they didn't have a stove. The songs were used for the women to get into the swing of the work. There was a tightening song."

"I can imagine what that was," said Mama. "Tightening your muscles to really get down to work."

"That's right," Papa agreed. "Then there were frolic songs, and they were to add a bit of fun right in the middle of the work. Then there were the stretching and clapping songs to make certain that the cloth was even. Then there was something called the consecration of the cloth because it was considered holy that one could finish it at all."

"You mean a consecration like in church?" I asked.

"Yes, there were many Catholics on the Island at that time," said Papa, "and they would even have the cloth blessed. And there was a blessing that went like this, 'The blessing of the Lord on this cloth, may the heroes wear it, enjoy it, by sea, by land, in the changes of mighty waves.' But it was the spinning songs that haunted me most. 'Hu ru rithil, thou the wheels and I the thread.'

"Sitting here of a Saturday night," said Papa, "I can hear it all come back. I must be getting very old. They say now, when you get very old, you can remember when you were very young."

"You're not as old as that, Papa," I said kindly.

"That sort of comment makes me feel even older." Papa sighed.

"Those old blessings had a nice ring to them," said Mama,

calling in from the kitchen. "I often thought making bread should have a song to it; the beating and the smoothing and the twirling and the rolling and the patting."

"Oh, it did, it did," said Papa. "There were many good baking songs."

"I like Saturday night," I said. "It seems so free."

"For a while, for a while," said Papa, "and then the kind of gloom of the Sabbath settles over it."

"There's no reason for any gloom," said Mama sharply.

"You know, Mama," Papa said, "I think that's the reason I married you. You're always the other side of the coin. I don't think you've ever had in your heart the gloom that we were born with. That's the difference in our geography. You were born with the color and light where I was born with darkness and night."

"You're very flattering this evening," said Mama.

"No, I mean it," said Papa. "We've always tried to seek out someone different from ourselves. That's the best way, lass— don't marry the similar; marry the different.

"Yes," Papa continued, "on a Saturday night you remember a lot. I think Burns knew that when he wrote 'The Cotter's Saturday Night.' And remembering long, long ago, I can remember my mother putting away the band around the spinning wheel at bedtime, because on Saturday night, of all nights, there were fairies."

"Oh, nonsense," said Mama.

"Yes, there were," said Papa. "Fairies who invaded the house and used the wheel after she would be long to bed. And that wasn't all. The bannock, a small cake, was made from the last trickle of meal at the end of the baking. You should do that right now. If you put a hole at the very end of it with your finger, you can that way keep the fairies away, or you can, if you like, put it under the stove."

"What a pile of nonsense," said Mama.

"I don't know about that," said Papa, helping Mama cover the bread, which would rise and be fresh and glowing in the morning. "I don't know about that, but I do know you ought to have a *glaistig,* one of those kitchen fairies, to help you in the kitchen."

"I don't need her," said Mama. "It isn't as though I do baking every day."

"And it isn't," said Papa, "as though you've got to do perpetual baking. You know, at home there used to be a story on the Isle of Harris in which an island woman was accosted by a fairy, who lured her to come in and see a sick person in the house. When she went in, she was ordered to make a loaf of bread for a huge company. They only gave her a handful or two of meal, and she was sure it would be an easy enough job, but the more she baked, the more meal remained; day after day and year after year she baked, and baked, and baked. She baked that way for years, and finally an old man hidden in the house called to her. 'What did they do to you?' She said, 'They asked me to come and attend a sick person.' 'And what did they ask you to do?' he said. 'Bake, bake, bake, eternally bake,' she said. 'And the more I bake, the more I have.' 'Bake once again,' said the old man, 'but the next time don't put a pickle of dusting meal back among the baking.' She did not. And, miracle of miracles, she was released from her chores."

"Oh, nobody lured me," said Mama. "I came of my own free will when I came to bake for the MacLeans."

"Well," said Papa, clapping her on the shoulder, "that's an honor to you, lass, an honor to you."

the letters

Almost as soon as we learned to write, we all acquired a vast range of international correspondence. I often have wondered how those various Scottish shopkeepers in Edinburgh, Glasgow, Aberdeen, and Inverness evaluated the juvenile correspondence they received from the United States, and if they realized what care and thought, yes, imagination too, had gone into the letters.

Our letters generally began:

Dear Sirs:
We have been in this country now for a number of years and long to see something of our homeland. Alas, we cannot get to Scotland, so Scotland must come to us. Please send us samples of the following tartans: Bruce, Campbell, Douglas, Grant, Stewart, Ewen.

We are domestics with a family in a Scottish colony in New York City.

120

Please pity us in our exile and send us samples posthaste . . .

"There," I said to my cousin Dotty, "I think that letter looks beautiful."

"Your handwriting doesn't look very elegant. It looks like —well, I hate to say it, but it looks like you're a kid."

"I am," I said simply.

"It shouldn't show. They're not going to send samples to anybody who's just a kid. It isn't like toothpaste, or something to develop your muscles. It's way across the seas, and they're just not going to do it."

My cousin, it seemed to me, was extremely officious. She was taller, smarter, older, stronger; goodness, there was practically nothing that she wasn't, but I did not feel that she could equal my compositions to the old country.

"I thought that was a lovely touch," I said, "about my being a domestic."

"Grandma would get sore at that," said Dotty. "She doesn't think you help at all, let alone ever being a servant."

"Do you think they would send us samples of anything else?"

"Such as what?" Dotty asked.

"You know, something important. Look at these pages."

We read the ads aloud very carefully.

" 'We always have in stock a good selection of skean dhus, dirks, sporrans, shoulder and bonnet brooches, silver pins, and clan badges, Balmoral and Glengarry bonnets, clan tartan hose, lace jabots, etc.' "

"They might send some etcetera," Dotty said, "but I wouldn't trust them."

The firms across the sea turned out to be more trustworthy than the letter writers. Over the months they carefully and patiently answered a great quantity of letters, each with its pathetic story about the anguish of the Depression or the difficulties of working for Americans, or the challenge of making a living on the hard stone streets of Manhattan, or the confusion of American manners and mores.

My imagination reached great heights of fantasy. We called ourselves by a variety of names—Peggy Stuart, Margaret Dineen, Bridie MacDougall, Jennifer Campbell, Jane Andrews —all in care of MacLean. We had an extraordinary range of characters in this elaborate fantasy, or if one preferred to call it such, fraud, that we conducted with the various tartan houses in England and Scotland.

As was inevitable, mail finally arrived for all these females, and Papa, quite startled, began to look into the matter.

"You better speak to Augie," said Mama. Augie was our postman. "We're getting the greatest collection of misdirected mail I've ever seen. One of these I've opened to make sure that something hadn't been misstamped, and look at it, will you?"

Out of it fell a great variety of tartans, all colors. The pieces were no bigger than penwipes, and, as a matter of fact, for a long time that's what I used them for. But we felt we had tapped generosity that we should share with others.

We took our friends into the secret of cooperative mail. Soon Johnny MacDonald was spending afternoons after school in the living room with us.

"They're all working on their homework together," said

Mama, when the neighbors asked about these afternoons. "It's really wonderful the way they inspire each other."

It was true that we were raised to great heights of inspiration.

"What I really want," said Johnny MacDonald, "is about twelve ells of good tartan."

"How much is an ell?" I asked.

"Forty-five inches in the dictionary," said Johnny. "But it's much more romantic to say 'ells'. I don't see anything very romantic about forty-five inches at all."

"That's the size of a grown man's tartan," I said. "You wouldn't need that much tartan, Johnny."

"Yes, I would. I've grown out of boy's kilts and all that kind of stuff. I'm either going to get a real hunting tartan or I'm never going to wear another one of the blasted things in my life. It's a crime the way the kids yell at us anyway on St. Andrew's Day."

We looked at Johnny MacDonald in satisfaction. "I'm going to propose to one of these companies," he said quite pontifically, "that they send me the ells I need on consignment."

Johnny's father was an advertising man, and it was obvious his vocabulary stretched in directions that we had not explored. "On consignment" was quite out of our comprehension.

"You mean without paying for it, Johnny?" I asked.

"I mean they can use the benefit of my opinion."

We had all benefited from Johnny's opinion from time to time. He was quite free with it.

"You know how they test things on expeditions and stuff

like that," said Johnny. "Like Admiral Byrd. Now Admiral Byrd took lots of things with him when he went to the South Pole, and those companies paid for the things he took. Then he'd test them, and if they were good, he'd say so and then they could advertise that it went with Byrd's expedition to the South Pole."

"You're not going anywhere, though, are you, Johnny?" queried my cousin.

"I'm going to do water testing," said Johnny.

"Make sure then," I said, "that you get a hunting tartan. That's better for work. It wouldn't do to be seen in a dress tartan when you're being serious."

"I need a hunting hat, too," said Johnny. "A good deer-stalking cap. They say to send your measurements and they make a fine one there up in Aberdeen."

"This is all going to cost you money," I said. "Johnny, you don't have any money, do you?"

"I have five dollars."

"Well, that will never be enough. Even after we calculate everything in pounds and shillings and pence, it's still going to be an awful lot of money they want for all this material."

"They'll want my opinion," said Johnny stubbornly. "They'll want my opinion."

Thereupon, Johnny wrote an extraordinary letter to a Scottish firm on St. Vincent's Street in Glasgow.

He chose Glasgow, he explained, instead of Edinburgh, because Glasgow seemed more adventurous.

"Edinburgh, my father says, is quite stuffy; but Glasgow—well, they know a bit more adventure when they see it."

124

Obviously Johnny and his father were right. The St. Vincent's Street company had an adventurous ad.

"We carry out every process from fleece to finished garment," it read. "Patterns or information sent with pleasure to any part of the world. We sell only quality goods which uphold the reputation and traditions of this old, established firm. We have been awarded gold medals in Edinburgh, in Paris prize medals in London, and a great award in Chicago."

"It's that Chicago award," said Johnny, "that wins me over. It goes to show you that they've got an interest in the New World and an interest in exploration. They won't be as stuffy perhaps as the rest of them."

"I wonder whom they sent tartan to in Chicago," my cousin asked. "Do you suppose it was a gangster?"

"It doesn't matter," said Johnny, "because they're going to be moved by my letter anyhow."

Johnny wrote: "MacDhomnuill-nan-Eilean-MacDonald of the Isles greets you. I am a direct descendant from Hugh, son of Alexander, Lord of the Isles. My father was Donald MacDonald. My grandfather was Alexander MacDonald. My great-grandfather was Angus MacDonald."

Johnny put down this beginning of his letter and studied it carefully. That Gaelic touch of MacDonald, Lord of the Isles, would, he felt, impress everyone, but I told him the handwriting was poor.

"Seon's right," said my cousin. "It doesn't look impressive and it should be an impressive letter, Johnny."

"I think it looks impressive," said Gogo. "I think it's a wonderful letter, Johnny."

"Yes, it is," said Johnny; "it's one of my best letters."

"Are you going to show it to your teacher, Johnny?" said Gogo. "Is it a composition?"

"It's far more than a composition," said Johnny. "It's probably the most important letter of my life. I suspect it will lead to great things."

"Just what are you going to ask for, Johnny?"

"I'm going to ask for twelve ells of cloth to test."

He took up the nib pen, rubbed it carefully with a piece of the tartan that I used for that purpose, juggled the bottle of ink as he did so, and another big spot splashed over the childishly lined paper.

"Having made my introductions," wrote Johnny, "I would like to tell you my intentions. It is my intention to honor you in an expedition I am about to undertake."

We were breathless in admiration. Papa had once shown me a copy of the ad that had appeared in the London *Times* when Shackleton was seeking fellow travelers to the South Pole. The stark simplicity of that ad was a little different from Johnny's more florid style, but I could sense in Johnny MacDonald's bosom the very same spirit. I hoped whatever Johnny planned to do would not go awry.

Johnny began to write again: "It is my purpose to test your tartan when used on an expedition involving water. You will remember that my family, the MacDonalds, have always been known as great mariners and have been closely related and associated with the sea. I am sometimes called," and he then brazened it out, "Captain MacDonald."

"It must be a composition," said Gogo; "it's just like a story."

"Be quiet," I said, "Johnny's writing."

"You will recall," wrote Johnny, "that in our glorious country's past, the tartan has kept off all manner of weather from the Highlander. It is my purpose on my expedition to wrap myself in a wet tartan each and every night for fourteen nights to test whether or not the fabric is sufficiently closely woven to give the same protection that it did when our sweet prince went out in '45."

Johnny closed this astonishing epistle with a great flowering display of English and a touch or two of Gaelic, which he copied out painstakingly from Father Dineen's Irish-English Dictionary. He thought, and he thought wisely, that whatever clerk read this letter—though, he said, you see I've addressed it to the director—would not know the difference between the Irish and the Scottish Gaelic, seeing that in this instance it varied only in a vowel or two.

"It's much too beautiful," I said, "to send like that. It's far too messy. Why don't we ask Papa to get his secretary to type it up?"

"I had planned to keep this a secret," said Johnny, for the first time sounding shy.

"Oh, Papa would call it a fine letter," I said. "It really is a fine letter, Johnny. None of my Peggy letters or Jennifer letters, or any of the letters that I did were nearly as good as this one. Come on, let's show him."

Papa was sitting in the front room in the large armchair on which you could press a button so that it would lean backward.

He had pressed that button and he was leaning backward, dreaming, it seemed to us as we entered the room, about the past. He awakened as soon as we reached his chair.

"Look at this wonderful letter Johnny has written, Papa," I said. "Do you suppose Miss Foulis could type it up for him?"

Papa read the letter, then took his glasses off and wiped them clean. "Truly a remarkable letter," he said, returning it to Johnny. "Truly a remarkable letter. Obviously, the MacDonald talent for words has found a new voice. You know your great-great uncle, Hugh MacDonald, Johnny, had such a braw of words that there was no one to touch him. He was Burns's greatest admirer. 'But Robbie,' he would say, 'Robbie is the greatest of them all.' Sometimes people would mention Keats, but Hugh would have none of it. 'Keats was a puir bit penny whistle of an English creature, not fit to hold a candle to Robbie. He gives ye nothing to get a grip on. It's thin, thin.' I'll always remember that remark. And you know, he was quite a critic. Burns is something to hold onto, and I'll tell ye, young Johnny, this letter is a piece to hold onto, too."

"We don't want to hold onto it, Papa," I said. "Johnny is going to send it to Glasgow."

"Oh, he is," said Papa. "And I suppose you think it's not quite neat enough or," and he looked at all of us, "maybe not grown up enough to send to Glasga the way it is. Is that true?"

"It's a wonderful letter," said Gogo. "I don't think it matters if it's messy. It's just wonderful."

"Well, it could stand a bit of improvement," said Papa. "Oh, not in style," he added quickly, watching Johnny's face, "not in style at all. I wouldn't think of changing a word. Perhaps a bit in the spelling or the punctuation. I believe Miss Foulis would be very interested in typing this letter and sending it off."

"Thank you, Mr. Mac," said Johnny. "Thank you very much. It's very important to my career."

"No doubt," said Papa, "no doubt at all about that."

The weeks stretched by, and Johnny and the rest of us grew alarmed over the inability of the Scots in the homeland to realize the seriousness and dedication of Johnny's offer.

When fall ended, Johnny was most disappointed. "What I was planning to do," he said, "was to roll up in Central Park and have you all throw buckets of water over me, and then I'd lie there for a few hours every day for two weeks, just the way I said I would."

"Your mother would give it to you," said my cousin. "She'd give it to you something awful."

"It's got nothing to do with my mother," said Johnny in disgust. "That's the way you conduct a scientific experiment, and that's what I'm going to do—conduct a scientific experiment of great importance."

"It's getting much too cold even to sit in Central Park," I said. "I don't see how you can go sleeping around there wrapped up in a wet piece of plaid."

"I know," said Johnny with disappointment. "It really is getting much too cold. If I got pneumonia, the whole purpose would go out of the test. I really would like to give them the benefit of my test. I do think they make a very good tartan, and in case of future battles or expeditions it would please me very, very much to tell the world how much I liked their plaid."

"Well, you won't get a chance to do anything," said Gogo, "unless it comes soon. Besides, maybe the plaid isn't any good. I don't see why you don't go to the park and wrap yourself in Jamie's old army blanket."

"You don't understand," said Johnny disgustedly. "You just don't understand."

The tartan came at last, twelve ells of it, exactly as Johnny had requested. We were astounded. It was obvious that the letter had deeply touched the heart of the director of Talbot Tartans. A letter from him came by separate cover.

"Dear Captain MacDonald," it said. "We are very impressed and pleased by your desire to test our tartan scientifically. We can assure you that it will stand up to the roughest treatment you choose to expose it to.

"We will be very glad to hear about the results of your experiments.

"Sincerely yours, J.C. Campbell, Director."

It was winter now, so Johnny couldn't take the heavy, rough plaid to Central Park. It would have been, as he pointed out, far too foolish, and besides his mother would never let him get out of the house with it. We had managed to smuggle it into his apartment and, putting our heads together—in this brief imaginative period Johnny let us participate in his experiment —we came to the conclusion that there was just one way in which he could test the material.

Each night while he took a bath, he soaked the tartan in the bathtub with him. Oh, not completely, just dropping it in until it was a little wet and pulling it out again. The bathtub was an old claw-footed treasure, with plenty of room beneath it, and during the day Johnny hid this damp and unwieldy covering deep within the space between the floor and the tub. Each night when the house was asleep, he lay for hours on the bathroom floor wrapped in his damp and eventually molding cloth.

"I thought of many things during those hours," he told us later. "I thought that I was a Greek on top of the mountains of Greece, or I thought I was with Napoleon's troops, or I was somebody out of James Fenimore Cooper. But mostly," he said, "I just thought I was with Wallace and Bruce, the greatest Scottish heroes."

In two weeks Johnny had a slight cold. The material was almost permanently damp and extremely dirty from the sessions under the tub, but the test, in Johnny's opinion, had been very successful.

"I wouldn't hesitate to say," said Johnny, "and I shall write Mr. Campbell to that effect, that it is suitable for any mariner's expedition I undertake."

It was my first witnessing of true scientific objectivity. And though, later on in my life, I was to see many examples of imagination, integrity, and industry at work in the testing of a product, I have never been more impressed than I was by Johnny MacDonald's fascinating excursion into the expedition of the bathroom floor.

When I discovered, much later, that Papa had actually paid for Johnny's tartan, it did not seem to affect the basic beauty of his experiments, nor the faith the Glasgow company had shown in him.

We thought it fair to tell Papa the whole story, and he was particularly enchanted by Johnny's adventure on the bathroom floor. And thereafter, whenever Papa saw him, he clapped him on the back and called him Johnny MacDonald, Lord of the Tiles.

"It's too bad," said Johnny, "there was no Gaelic word for the tiles."

"Or for that matter," said Papa, "there wasn't originally even a Gaelic word for bathroom."

heritage

Papa in his flights of Celtic fancy had convinced me that he was descended from the family of St. Columba, the Irish Saint who went to the Scottish Islands in the ninth century.

Agnes Kennedy denied it. Agnes Kennedy, all pink—pink hair, pink freckles, pink cheeks—puffing in the cold, stood half buried behind her mother. She ducked her head out regularly, like a fan, teasing the conversation, stirring up the wind of controversy over the brownstone porches on our street.

"St. Columba is a holy saint," Agnes contributed.

"If you know so much, why aren't you smart?" I snapped. Then I said to her mother as respectfully as I could, "Presbyterians don't have any saints." I was surprised at the sound in my voice. It was touched with disappointment. Why didn't we have saints? It was a great pity. My religion left me at a terrible disadvantage in our neighborhood.

"Oh, it's not your fault, child," Mrs. Kennedy replied. "It was the way you were brought up."

I bristled again. Or rather my coat and sweater bristled. I was mad. My sweater felt like a hair shirt; it itched.

"You can't help it. We know you girls can't help it," Agnes said, popping her head out. "People that don't have saints just can't help it, can they, Mother?"

"Give me ree-gards to your grandmother," said Mrs. Kennedy. "Come along, along, Agnes."

"Come along, along, Agnes," I mimicked to myself. "Give my ree-gards to," but my humor changed suddenly, and I went into the house, singing at the top of my voice, " 'Give my ree-gards to Broadway.' "

"A little lower," said Mama.

"Mama," I challenged, "have *you* ever known a saint?"

"You don't exactly *know* a saint," Mama countered. "Who were you talking to on the street? I caught a glimpse from the window."

"Mrs. Kennedy."

"Well." Mama laughed. "You don't have to worry about *that* saint."

"Where's Gogo?" I said.

"Playing at Mary Finnegan's house."

"I'll pick her up," I volunteered.

"You're not practicing, Seon, are you?"

"Practicing what, Mama?"

"Practicing to be a saint."

I closed the door carefully behind me. Mama annoyed me at times. She just wasn't serious. How could she joke about important things? Was she really concerned about the state of our souls?

I thought a great deal about our souls. Not just my soul. Not just Gogo's soul. But everybody's. Papa's soul, for example. When I was little, I thought maybe I could see it. Like a wisp of smoke hovering around his head, sucked in each time when he drew upon his pipe. Papa's soul was a wisp, like Scottish fog. It danced and sang.

"Give my ree-gards to Broadway."

I was walking on Broadway now. At the corner of Ninety-third Street there was a five-and-ten that distracted me momentarily from my concern with the spirit. The body, too, had demands. It was nearly Passover. What an exciting holiday. Far more exciting than Easter.

The five-and-ten always seemed far more aware of the calendar than any other shop. You could go into it early in October, for example, never thinking of Halloween, and suddenly, almost jumping out at you, a black cardboard cat bounced in front of your eyes. Halloween had a different smell from Easter's—a smell of hard corn candy, gay, crusty, as orange as a harvest moon. Of course the five-and-ten always had a smell particularly its own. A wisp of stale air, a smear of oilcloth, the joy of people, the glory of extravagance. There was no frustration here. What you saw, you could generally buy. Papa said the United States had given the world two things: The Bill of Rights and the five-and-ten. They were the bargains of the world.

I wandered up and down the aisles—lifting, weighing, comparing. I held fair jewels up to the light, clipped on earrings, smiled at myself in the tiny oval mirrors that reflected back my first glimpse of adolescence.

"Just looking, thanks."

Up and down the aisles I went, dreaming in that Never-Never land made up of current heroines: Queen Mary and Joan Crawford.

I had thought a lot about their souls. Queen Mary, big-bosomed, crowned with wisdom (was that *her* soul glittering like tiny lights in her tiara—as sparkling as five-and-ten diamonds). Joan, Joan Crawford. I caught a glance of myself in another detour around the jewelry counter. I "flashed" a smile. I wasn't quite sure how you flashed one, but Joan did, all the time. It came to me suddenly that *her* soul was in her teeth, shining with toothpaste, white and fair as moonlight. I had no chance—small-bosomed, crooked teeth.

("False values," Papa had roared when I complained. "False values. You've got the MacLean teeth. They've been biting off chunks of life while the rest of the world sucks at the pap of false values.")

Maybe, I thought now, maybe he was right. But it did seem unfair. Small-bosomed, crooked teeth, and no saints.

St. Joan. Did Joan of Arc suffer in this way? Unappreciated, undiscovered. I stood stock-still to see if I could hear voices.

"Did you want something?"

"Everything," I wanted to cry. But could I get everything in the five-and-ten? Curly hair and straight teeth, glamour and wisdom?

"I'll take these," I said.

The salesgirl slipped my purchase in a bag and mumbled kindly, "Wear them in good health."

It was a nice expression. The Scots and Irish had no expression to compare with it. The Jews were very, very lucky, and besides they had Passover. I looked at the salesgirl carefully. What about her soul? I thought I could see it glitter in her rhinestone pin.

Small-bosomed, crooked teeth, no saints, no rhinestone.

I took out the long white gloves that I had just bought. I put them on my fingers carefully, slowly, the way Aunt Fiona had taught me; push, twist, turn, until all my fingers felt trapped into the gentle confines of growing up. I looked into the full-length mirror at the front of the store. The saddle shoes didn't look quite right, but the gloves were wonderful. I took my coat off just to see how they crawled up my arms like stockings. I practiced a regal salute with my hand—a rigid elbow, an easy wrist, a quick curve of the hand. Queen Mary really had it down just right. I sighed. Of course you really needed to wave from a royal carriage to give the whole scene meaning. But there was one thing—Queen Mary hadn't been descended from St. Columba's family.

the auld lang pampas

Scots are inveterate joiners. They dis-
criminate in one way only—the organizations must be Scottish. Papa, a transplanted Scot in New York, belonged to a
minimum of sixteen clubs. There were clubs of clans and clubs
of septs, there was the Grand Order of Caledonia and the Scottish Sons (and Daughters) of Liberty. There was the Robert
Burns Society, where all of us attempted a poor brand of Lal-
lans—that hybrid tongue of the Lowlands—and then the
Highland clubs where the piebrochs or bagpipes wailed at
births and anniversaries, holidays and graduations, weddings
and the annual ceildhes, and, with terrible finality, wailed out
the death of a loyal member. Some Scots would join Scottish
organizations in other parts of the world—affiliated groups
that circled the world with New Year haggis and Auld Lang
Syne. Attendance was by correspondence only, but they were

good letter writers, those faraway Scots in New Zealand, Australia, Kenya. But none were as good, as romantic, as colorful in my childhood eyes as Uncle Malcolm. Uncle Malcolm lived in the Argentine.

My circumspect view of New York in those days was as distorted as those fabulous maps: The Bostonian's idea of the world, the Texan's idea of the universe. New York was mostly made up of Scots; all Scots were in the importing business; every Scot would, of course, go home someday. Home was very far away indeed. Home was Scotland. On the other hand, the Scots had reconciled themselves to New York, produced American children, and acclimated themselves to their American world by transforming the environment with holidays and kilts into a reasonable facsimile of home.

It was quite different for Uncle Malcolm. The Argentine was definitely *not* Scotland, wrote Uncle Malcolm. It was a question of language. "Aye, and a terrible confusion it is. After ten years here, I speak Spanish well enough. But Henrietta has refused to utter as much as a word. The boys, however, and there's the rub, are practically foreigners. They refuse, *defiantly* refuse, to speak English at table. I can't tell you what a curious sensation this is. I feel I have spawned gauchos instead of Scots."

The loyalty among Scots is proverbial. Something had to be done about Uncle Malcolm's boys.

It was decided in due course that the Order would sponsor a visit. It did not occur to anyone that Scotland might be more beneficial than New York. Deep down in every heart was the belief that the good Scot, the enterprising one, naturally left home . . . and that the very best Scots were in New York. And we did speak English at table. Unfortunately, there weren't enough funds for the three boys. Finally, they decided to propose the visit to Duncan, the middle boy—the Scot's view of justice being if you can't be on either side, you can always be in the middle.

I was filled with delight. Loving Humphrey Bogart from the front row of a movie theater had been very unrewarding. Besides it hurt my eyes. I knew deep down I was ready for a gaucho. I was very confused about just what a gaucho was, but I applied myself to finding out. Then I could share his interests. I hoped Duncan would like girls.

For a month I went around the house in a Latin daze. I learned *¿Cómo está usted? Muy bien. Adiós.* I repeated the words with different inflections of mouth, nose, and eyebrows. I fancied myself in shawls and tall combs, and sang "My Bonnie Lies over the Ocean" with all the aggressiveness Scots put into the songs they have learned from the nursery. I was in love with an exotic foreigner.

Duncan made the long trip by cattle boat. By the time his ship docked, my ardor had been replaced by information. Gauchos, I had discovered, were really nothing but cowboys. This had come as a great disappointment. Cowboys really didn't interest me. Of course, the Argentinian cowboys were a little different. They were a kind of mixture—part Indian, part Spanish. At home in the towns, at home on the pampas. And yet, maybe, like people so easily at home—at home nowhere.

the auld lang pampas

Just riding, riding, riding into imaginary sunsets. It was romantic, but it was sad, too, just as sad as it could be.

I even forgot to say *¿Cómo está usted?* when I met him. He was an inch shorter than I, and besides he did speak perfect English and looked just like a Scot. It was kind of disappointing.

Duncan was a great disappointment, too, to the Order. They had nothing to teach him. If possible, he knew more about Scotland than they did. Why, he even had a smattering of Gaelic. Duncan and I, on the other hand, had a lot of fun in the dark excitement of Radio City Music Hall. Such gay abandon leads to confidences.

"Don't you think," said Duncan, "they're all a little silly?"

"Movies are silly," I said defensively, "but I do like them."

"Oh, I didn't mean the movies. I mean our families. Families come close to being just plain weird. Particularly Scottish families. Look at me. I'm not a Scot, you know. Oh, I can pretend all right. And I do like the songs and bagpipes. But really, I'm an Anglo-Argentinian. That's what I am."

"I guess I'm really Scottish-American," I said speculatively.

"Of course. And when you grow up you'll be American and I'll be Argentinian."

I hadn't thought of it quite that way. I hadn't realized—or wanted to face it perhaps—that the dream of Scotland in which our families lived was a kind of chrysalis which we'd have to abandon. But Duncan knew. I looked at him admiringly.

"I've got it all worked out," he continued. "It all depends on

143

your mother tongue. English is yours, so it won't be so much of a problem. But for me, it's different. Mine is Spanish. That makes me really different."

I wondered if Duncan would change; grow darker and darker. Come to think of it, he did look different already.

When we took Duncan to the boat, the entire Order turned out. There was no doubt about it. Duncan would be a confirmed Scot, re-creating a part of Scotland deep in a Latin world.

Uncle Malcolm was deeply impressed. Duncan was now willing to speak English at table, and the other two boys soon followed suit. The Order applauded itself with Messianic glee.

Duncan and I exchanged notes over the years. I was very gaucho, he said—a really good guy even if I was a girl. But one year his Christmas card read, "from your Argentinian friend." From then on, I signed mine, "Seon, the American."

rob roy's children

In the long summer days when one is growing up, boredom and tedium are as omnipresent as the oppressive sun that shines and shines with frightening regularity. I was glad that our August boredom was shattered by the noise of the MacGregor children, stepping-stones from age ten down to two, whom I explained to Mama had an extraordinary heritage.

I had to be patient with Mama. She was remarkably insensitive to the great chord of Scottish history that I sounded day and night. I had read somewhere that Sir Walter Scott's hero, the great Rob Roy, had been a MacGregor. It was obvious that Mama was unaware that the MacGregor children, whom the neighborhood declared to be pests, brats, and a general nuisance, were of a blood so remarkable that if they cut themselves climbing Mrs. MacAllister's apple tree, a red gorse bush would probably spring from the drops of their blood.

"I feel sorry for the MacGregors, Mama. You know they lost their name."

"What do you mean, they lost their name? They seem to me to have extraordinary names. Diana, Demeter, and Prometheus. I don't know what ever occurred to Margaret Mac-Gregor to blossom into such nomenclature."

"I think they're wonderful names. Diana makes me think of a Greek goddess. Can't you just see a Greek goddess, Mama, with her veils floating in the wind?"

"Nonsense," said Mama abruptly. "You're thinking of Isadora Duncan, and she's not a suitable person for any young girl to be thinking about. I think Diana is really a scandalous name."

I paid no attention and continued to contemplate the remarkable MacGregors.

"And Demeter," I continued, "Demeter is really the most glorious of all names. Doesn't it mean something about the harvest?"

"Not a good old American harvest. And besides, they are *not* church names. They don't have the ring of a good church name. I can't imagine anybody being christened Diana, Demeter, or Prometheus. Prometheus," she said scornfully. "I don't believe I've ever heard such nonsense. He's such a little boy, and such a nasty little boy, too."

"He's only five," I said. "Five-year-old boys, I guess, are pretty much of a nuisance."

"That five-year-old boy," said Mama, "Prometheus or no Prometheus, should learn to keep his drawers on. Margaret lets him walk and run around these lawns without a stitch on."

"Prometheus was a Greek god, Mama."

"Well, that little savage has a long way to go before there will be any Greek godding him."

"He's a little like Pan, isn't he, Mama? Wouldn't you say he's a little like Pan or Puck?"

"He's a little up-to-no-good, that's what," said Mama.

"Still," I said, "I always feel sorry for the MacGregors."

"There's no reason," said Mama, "to feel sorry for them. You can believe me, they are not feeling sorry for anybody else. They just lead a life all their own."

"I like their house," I said. "I wish we lived in a carriage house, with old rickety-rackety stairs and balconies and all those magnificent roses tumbling down."

"That's just it, child. The whole house is tumbling down. The children are tumbling down those rickety-rackety stairs faster than the rain on a July day."

"It's a romantic house, and the MacGregors seem so romantic."

"Nonsense. If poor and messy and shaggy puppies are romantic, then I guess they are, but they certainly don't seem very romantic to me. You know, Seon, you can give your children fancy names, but don't expect the world to sit back and pay homage to them just because you discovered the dictionary.

"Just look at their front yard," added Mama. "We all like our yards to be a little different. That is, I grow my dahlias and Mrs. MacAllister grows her delphinium. Some of us like portulaca, some of us don't. I myself have a horror of snowballs, but Mrs. MacTavish seems to think that they are the Lord's gift to the garden. I love petunias, but I don't want to drown in them like the Campbells. To be different—well, that's just human individuality. But I am against it when you are just so human individual that you don't care about anybody else at all."

I looked down the street to the MacGregor house. It was not an easy house to see. It was nestled in a clump of trees and shrubs. It appeared to have slid down the hill to the railroad track, and the back porch nestled in cattails and swamp cabbage. Each year the house seemed to be moving closer to the trestles. I expected to come down from the city one year and discover that all the MacGregors had disappeared. They would be picked up, as a cow might be, on the cow catcher in front of one of the trains and be deposited haphazardly at the end of the railroad line. There, in southern New Jersey, house, mother, father, and children would all stay just as they had been tossed—never looking for permanence because to MacGregors there was no permanence. Every day was an exciting adventure. Never looking for "their place in society" because all society to them was so much nonsense. Never looking for security because none of them had ever known it long enough to ever look for it again. When the world gives you nothing, you expect nothing, and that was part of the romance of the MacGregors to me. They expected nothing and so they did not look for those unobtainable things that haunt the rest of us, not only in childhood but in adolescence and adulthood— those vague items that we never give up looking for, that make our lives fraught with both excitement and despair. It seemed to me that the MacGregors looked for only two things, hollyhocks and sunflowers. Their side yard was alive with sunflowers. They reached almost to the second story of the carriage house. And where the rest of the neighborhood exhibited its individuality in the turn of an iris walk and a new type rose, the MacGregors simply planted two more rows of hollyhocks. All they wanted were sunflowers and hollyhocks.

"And," said Mama, "what they want, they take."

It was true that the MacGregors had been known to trespass on everybody's lawn, even Mrs. MacAllister's back garden, and there in the dead of the night to pick out new hollyhocks from last year's planting.

"Everything they have," said Mama, "comes from somebody else."

"I think, Mama, it's because they lost their name."

"Whatever is this child talking about, Joseph? She keeps harping on the MacGregors and something about their losing their name. You've a one-track mind, Seon, and half the time I don't even know what's on that one track. It's exactly like a railroad track that's going nowhere."

"I said the MacGregors lost their name, and they did lose their name, didn't they, Papa?"

"Well," said Papa, not anxious to be drawn into the conversation, "that was a long time ago."

"They've only been here five years," said Mama. "When old lady Clymer sold that property, she sold it just to spite everybody else on the street."

"It was far more than five years ago, Mama. They lost it

centuries ago, didn't they, Papa? They lost it during the times of Troubles, two hundred years ago."

Papa went into the kitchen to get himself a cup of tea. He spent an eternity, it seemed to me, lighting the fire underneath the kettle, examining the enamel boxes where we kept each tea separately and individually so it could not be contaminated by its brethren. He poked into the higher reaches of the closet for a brown sugar that, he decided, was the only thing to sweeten a new Ceylonese brew. Then we heard a great clatter as he reached for something in Mama's old brown closet. That closet was a source of infinite mystery and excitement to me, because it contained the cookbook that had belonged not to Mama's mother, but to her mother's mother, and wonders and wonders, to her mother before her. It was aged and cracked and the paper fell apart in one's hands. Once a year we were allowed to take it down. Placed on the kitchen table, each page was turned not with our fingers but with a fat, round-headed knife as heavy as age itself.

In that brown closet, Papa found the finest of Mama's eight porcelain cups, dropped in a spray of brown sugar, and then poured, piping hot, his Ceylon tea from the old brown tea jug.

"You didn't answer my question, Papa," I said. "Didn't the MacGregors lose their name?"

"You've got to be patient," said Papa, "when you make a cup of tea. People rush a cup of tea. You cannot hurry too much for comfort. You can't, Seon, hurry too much for wisdom. The mind is a little like an old, fragile porcelain cup. First you have to cradle it, then you have to be sure just what you will put into it, then you have to sweeten and temper it—

only then are you capable of ever tasting it, let alone digesting it."

"I can't blame the girl," said Mama, "wanting a straight answer to a straight question. You look at life, Joe, as though it had more sides than an octagonal playhouse. You'll trip over your vocabulary someday and fall right on your period."

Papa laughed. "Look out the window, Bertha," he said. "I think Prometheus MacGregor is in the garden again."

"No," cried Mama. "No!"

She lunged for the door. She had on an apron gaily patterned with crab apples, and she swished it in front of her as though chasing chickens. "Out of here, Prometheus."

Prometheus MacGregor stood grinning at her, his ears as defiant as his laugh, and his strong baby teeth challenging the authority that was pursuing him.

"I'll make you . . ." roared Mama. "I'll make you mincemeat."

"I didn't mean it, Mrs. Mac. I was only helping the flowers to grow."

His sudden hysterics startled Mama.

"Don't cry, Prometheus. Here's a handkerchief. Now wipe your nose. Pick up your pants, come on now, pick up your pants. A Japanese beetle went up the leg."

"Can I have a cookie? Could I have one of those spiced cookies?"

"Of course you can," Mama said gently. "Now come along."

She went around to the back porch and into the still room. There she dried Prometheus' tears and gave him a small sack of spiced cookies and, for good measure, three bottles of her best root beer.

"Mama gives away more root beer," I said crossly, "than we ever drink."

"That's no way to talk," said Papa. "You ought to be glad to share what you have."

"I share most everything, but I don't like to share root beer. Mama's root beer bubbles better than any other root beer I ever had."

"Your grandmother is a very remarkable woman."

"Why did the MacGregors lose their name, Papa?"

Papa sat at the table, staring at his tea quietly.

"You know, Seon, to be frank, I've forgotten all about the MacGregors. What is all this about the MacGregors and their name?"

"Well," I said smugly, "during the time of the Risings, the MacGregors not only lost their right to speak Gaelic and the right to wear their tartans, but they also lost the right to use their name. And in all of Scotland the name MacGregor was not allowed to be spoken. You knew that, didn't you, Papa?"

"I recall now, but I can't for the life of me recall the pecks of Scottish this and Scottish that you've acquired like a young bird about to build her nest. Besides," he continued, "how do you think that fits in with these MacGregors?"

"Aren't all the MacGregors the same, Papa? Aren't we all one great big clan?"

"We are all one great big clan," said Papa, "true enough, but that phraseology is more Baptist than Presbyterian. You always get a little Baptist indoctrination down here every summer, don't you, Seon? And I suppose you see us all as one great big clan marching to the drums of the Lord, all going to heaven, one nation indivisible."

"John the Baptist," I said, "was a salesman of the Lord."

"Where did you acquire that piece of merchandising?"

"The Tanners say so. The Tanners say they would be very glad to have the MacGregors come to church. They say the Baptists make room for everybody. And they could make room in the Lord's bosom for the MacGregors just as well as for anyone else. Mrs. MacGregor says she always used to send the children to the Baptist Sunday School, but now people have given them such nice hand-me-downs, she thinks it's fitting for them to go to the Presbyterian."

Mama came into the room, and I was pleased to hear that her crab-apple apron clanked with the sound of some bottles.

"Here's your root beer—I hope you enjoy it as much as those poor children."

"Their trouble started, Mama, when they lost their name. They wanted to follow the king, you know, and they were punished for it, and they lost their name and no one could utter it."

"Is that true, Joe?" said Mama, picking up interest.

"Oh, that's true enough," said Papa. "I had forgotten it, but it was common knowledge at one time."

"Poor souls," Mama said. "Maybe they have a sense of inferiority. Would you think that would be the reason, Joe, for all their miseries?"

"You can't say that these MacGregors are the same as all

MacGregors," Papa reminded her. "For all we know, they've never seen the dust of Scotland for a generation or two."

"Oh, that's true," said Mama. "They come from around Farmingdale, you know, and I think they have been here for a good couple of hundred years. But the way I look at it, Joseph, is that if you lose something, you're always searching for it again. Probably that's the reason they take such liberties picking up people's hollyhocks."

"I don't see the similarity between losing your name generations ago in a time of trouble in Scotland and being free and easy with other people's flowers today."

"Oh, I do," said Mama. "I do."

And I could tell she did. Mama had some gift of understanding that eluded the rest of us. We usually needed an intellectual evaluation to arrive at the spontaneous blossom of sweet decision that flowered so easily from Mama.

"Not only," she continued, "do I understand about the hollyhocks (and the truth is all they had to do was ask for them and Mrs. MacAllister and I would give them half the garden), but I understand about the drawers."

"The drawers?"

"Yes, the boy's drawers."

"The breeks of young Prometheus? What has that got to do with this ancient law and legend of another clime?"

"Speak American," said Mama. "It's easy enough to understand about the boy's drawers."

"Explain it then," said Papa.

"You said they lost their language, right?"

"Yes, that's true enough."

"Well, they are all extremely odd with language. Sometimes a little violent, and that must be because they lost the language once. Don't you see, Joe?"

"Yes," said Papa, following Mama's conversation carefully and tapping off each point with a silver teaspoon against his cup.

"You say they lost their tartans, right?"

"Right."

"That explains it," said Mama. "Once you've lost your tartans—the clothes you wear—you care little enough about your drawers, isn't that true, Joe?"

Papa looked startled as he replied, "That's naked truth, Mama. Naked truth."

the cityscapes

The city was a different landscape. Almost a Scottish fog enveloped us in the park on a soft, early spring night. We would sit with Mr. Frazer, with Mr. Ferguson, with Mr. MacAllister on the rough benches of Central Park and watch the mist rise gently over the reservoir. We would climb the rock in the upper reaches of the park, scaling the rough surface of childhood, scraping our memories and our shoes against the rock and shale of the past. Careful. All of us can turn an ankle on the pebbles of yesterday. Careful. This stone can avalanche. Careful. We are all like Sisyphus rolling our stones up hill. Or so said Mr. Frazer, or Mr. Ferguson, or Mr. MacAllister.

"But remember, Seon," said Mr. MacAllister, "there are no storytellers like the Celts; there are no heroes like the Gaels. There are no lands like our ancient lands."

I was venturing out into the world of adolescent rebellion,

thrusting one toe forward to test the water, snatching it back
from the current of icy reality, losing my balance between
right and wrong, between childhood and girlhood, between
the past and tomorrow. I struck out indefinitely and alone. Not
really alone, because I took with me Skippy MacKenzie, my
dog and confidant. Skippy whimpered for the world outside
just as I did. I leashed him and walked him through all the
forbidden paths.

I was finding my own lands—the reaches of Columbus Avenue.

It was appropriately named, I thought. One had to be an
explorer to venture into its interior. There was no exterior at
all. If you looked heavenward, the buildings came together—
parallel lines meeting not in infinity, but here, before your
eyes, in a rush of astigmatism and city shadows. Above our
heads the El rushed by, screeching only occasionally as it
groaned to a standstill at the station in the sky. The stairs to
those stations looked precarious, unreal. The whole El seemed
unreal from our vantage point on the ground. Skippy barked
as the trains went past—but they disappeared so rapidly in the
sky, he seemed to feel his barks uselessly challenged some
heavenly ghost, and he sat back on his haunches. Dismay
sealed him to the sidewalk. I had to pull his leash to move him.
Then I gathered him in my arms—comfort for us both, as we
moved, block by block, away from home territory.

The horseradish woman was always under the El at Ninety-
ninth Street. She was far more reliable than the street signs
that the boys twisted on Halloween so that street directions
were forever at variance with the truth. Not the horseradish

lady. Her truth was as sharp and pungent in the mouth as her wares. In the winter she diversified, an entrenched entrepreneur, and in addition to the horseradish roots in the great wicker basket at her feet, she presided over a charcoal burner with chestnuts bursting in the heat. Her feet—she seemed just feet and head—were wrapped in great woolen scarves and placed squarely on a pile of newspapers that served as both footrest and wrapping counter. Her movements were all ritual. She stripped a corner from the morgue of yesterday's news, and with one motion wrapped the horseradish root, or the handful of chestnuts, as skillfully, I thought, as a cowboy rolling a cigarette in the Saturday-afternoon movie at the Thalia. If you cared to wait, she would grate the horseradish; grate it as coarsely as the light that made a ragged, torn path through the slats of the El overhead. Her face—it was an extraordinary one, a face I saw over and over again later as the Russian world moved into the newsreels—was a face that labored, warred, screamed out at the world's injustice, and yet was silent, a face so silent that over all the years I frequented that spot, I heard her say only a few words.

To Mama she said, "Yes, lady?"

To me, not yet a lady, not perhaps even worthy of affirmation or denial, she asked only one word: "Grated?"

Was that what she asked of the world from this dark corner? Or was that what the world asked of her? Grated, scraped, uprooted as the roots she sold.

Mr. Dietrick on another dark corner had no such air about him at all. The horseradish lady was head and feet, but Mr.

Dietrick was head and body—with no feet at all. Or, as Gogo said, all his feet were in the window.

Rows and rows of pigs' feet.

Mama said it was a rude joke—but we children thought it pretty funny. It was like dogs, we decided—people and dogs grew to look alike.

"Why look at you, Seon," said Gogo. "You've got crazy, mixed-up spaniel hair like Skippy's. And maybe fleas."

So it was natural that Mr. Dietrick might take on some aspects of his pork shop. Behind that great concealing counter, he walked on pig's feet like a Disney cartoon. His cheeks were as flushed as spiced sausage; his fingers, chubby and tan as frankfurters; and, said Gogo, experimenting with language as I was experimenting with independence, "He's full of baloney."

Our world was beginning to change. Once Mr. Dietrick had been a hero to us, generosity itself, and that piece of baloney that he extended to a waiting child was one of the rewards of life itself. You didn't have to do anything for Mr. Dietrick's baloney. He just gave it to you. For nothing. He didn't ask whether you had been good or bad. What were your marks? Nothing. If you existed, you were entitled to baloney. Free.

Mama said we shouldn't get wrong ideas. Nothing was free in the world. Except, amended Papa, a dream or two.

"Not even that," said Mama. "We pay for dreams."

"That's true," Papa agreed sadly. "Your grandmother's right. Look at Margaret Farrell. She's paid for her dream."

And so did Mr. Dietrick. Over many a slice of baloney, we

had heard his story. How he had arrived in the country as a boy from Germany—his father never letting out of his grasp that weather-bent cardboard case that sheltered a million marks. The mark, swore Mr. Dietrick's father, was the only security in the world. The marks, of course, failed him; life failed him—but he passed some of his obsession on to his son.

When I returned once to the old landscapes just before I entered college, that Dietrick dream had taken a new shape, a new face, a bristled mustache every bit as sharp as the pig's bristle in the window. The photograph of the new face was affixed to the inner side of the huge, cold, meat chest. I could see it each time Mr. Dietrick opened the door to a dream of ice—Adolf Hitler.

The landscape of Ninety-eighth Street was completely out of bounds. From Columbus Avenue to Amsterdam Avenue the street was, Papa explained, as bad as the Gorbals. A true slum.

"Stay out of it, lass. It gives Glasga a regular run for its money."

And I did run through it from time to time—just to see if I would be pursued by all the evils of the world.

I was never chased by anyone except once by Willie Kennedy on Halloween. Willie Kennedy's mind was "slow," but his feet were fast enough, and he successfully bashed me with a stocking full of flour, and I went home more guilty than afraid for Willie never left Ninety-eighth Street. If I were to say who the culprit was, I would reveal my own indiscretion.

It was more, of course, than indiscretion. It was wild, high, feverish adventure that turned my heels to Ninety-eighth Street. The New York Gorbals, as Papa called it, was not really like its Glasgow companion. In Glasgow that famous slum was imprisoned in charcoal and obscenity. Ninety-eighth Street, I found, was simply imprisoned in poverty. A poverty that differed from the Depression—we all left toothbites in Depression apples. The bites in Ninety-eighth Street were never to be mentioned.

Bedbugs and fleas and ——

On a mild day, huge mothers sat on the brown front stoops and combed the hair of their daughters seated on the steps below. Occasionally they bashed them with the flat of their hand or the hairbrush—and occasionally their strength and indignation was such that an unwary child toppled from the porch. But I could see—from the newspaper store on the corner—that this was Mother Love, and that mother and child were held by some great, indefinable bond, and that all the slaps and laments did not shake the faith of each to each. They had something that Gogo and I did not have.

Their own, very own mother.

Gogo did not join me in these sentiments—and when she got old enough to accompany me in the excursion for the paper, she told me just what these mothers and children did have.

"Head lice," said Gogo. "Don't you smell the turpentine? That's for cooties."

I looked at Gogo, astonished. How, and where, and with what ease she acquired her knowledge of the everyday world astonished me.

"How do you know?"

"I just know. I just know, that's all."

My idyllic, sentimental picture of mother and child on the brown stoops of New York never recovered from Gogo's worldly knowledge, but no revelations could shatter my belief in Jennie Dundee.

Jennie Dundee lived on the corner of Ninety-eighth and Columbus Avenue on the fourth floor of a tenement that, like some seeking child, seemed to reach out for the racing El just beyond the parlor window. Jennie ignored the El. She had grown up ignoring the world with the same ease and grace with which the world had ignored her. When she was eight, Jennie's parents had, she said, been taken from the world.

"Oh, don't fret, lass," Jennie said to me. "They were bums, both of them. The greatest drifters of the Gorbals."

Jennie had come from the Gorbals.

"Don't ever mention Scotland to me," she said. "And don't ever mention love to me. There are those what can afford love. I can't afford love and I can't afford the past. Oh, I know why your grandmother lets you come to see me occasionally. It's to get me in the church, that's why. If they get me in a church again, I'll be dead. Never before. You'd think Jesus Christ was a Scot according to the bunch of them. And the life hereafter is a regular gathering of the clans, I suppose."

"No," I protested.

"You're young."

Jennie Dundee had one great desire. It was to sing in the amateur night at the theater on Broadway. She had a spectacular voice, warm and rich (like Dundee cake, I thought) and smoky as peat.

" 'My mother had three butter platies,' " she sang as she

gathered the tea things. "Ay, platies. 'My mother had three butter platies. And she's got nae other daughter but me.'"

"Amateur night," said Jennie, "is better than plate night. And plate night, lass, you can come away with a set of plates if you've a mind."

It was a hot Wednesday night—when Jennie Dundee sang at the amateur night at the local movie theater on Broadway.

The whole world was there. Certainly all of Ninety-eighth Street, most of our street, and even church members from as far away as Forest Hills were there. And, to even things out, so were the Catholic nuns from the neighborhood.

Broadway was a completely different landscape. It was strange to see these familiar faces in a place that courted the unfamiliar. I had teethed my first growing-up fantasies on the popcorn and dreams of this very movie, where on the screen every face and figure was larger than life size. The Depression was forgotten by everyone in the fierce gaze of Humphrey Bogart. This was, I thought, the temple of sophistication and, for one wretched, miserable moment, I was filled with embarrassment and shame for Jennie.

Could she fit in here? In this glamorous world of movie stars and overpowering newsreels that sucked all into a world far away. Here the camera rolled and life screamed out the story of a new Cuban Revolution, here we saw the death of a king—Alexander of Yugoslavia—right before our eyes (it was fitting, said Mrs. Connelly), and to temper it all, the Dionne quintuplets crawled into every heart. This was the temple of truth.

Jennie's competition, I decided, was just too much. Jennie

was no Jean Harlow. Her hair was black as night. Her body was big and bold, her face too wide, the cleft in her chin more scar than dimple, her hands too fierce. She had grappled with too much, too young. No part of her surely was as God had meant it to be.

Except her voice.

The old Scots used to say God honeyed the voice of an orphan. It had honeyed and sharpened and glorified Jennie's voice—and the fog of the Clyde had done the rest. As she sang, you could taste her voice, you could savor it. She dipped into a honey pot—slowly, deliberately. The songs she sang had all the monotony of tragedy—the ballads bled and cried, wailed and whimpered.

The audience that night had let her go on and on without interruption. Jennie had always been interrupted. Her life had been nothing except tragic interruption but, through it all, something continually deep within chained her to music that was older than time. She had a sense of timing, too. When the audience could stand no more, she changed her pace, put her hands on her hips, and sang:

I ken whaun I'm gaun
But you're no comin' wi' me
I've a lad o' my ain
An ye daurnae tak him frae me.

He wears a tartan kilt,
He wears it in the fashion—

And every time he birls aroon'
You'd burst your sides wi' laughin'.

And laugh we did. Jennie knew where she was going. She went a long way—and it was gentle irony that her voice rang out in every Scottish house of worship from Inverness, California, to sheep-herding stations in Montana.

She and the other Scots knew where they were going—they were becoming part of America.

the return

"It's probably changed so," said Papa, "that I wouldn't recognize it, but it doesn't matter. I want to see it anyway."

"You'd be cold," Mama said. "You're not used to cold summers. You'd better take a good heavy coat and your winter suits; I'll get them out of the cleaner's."

"I'm not going to the North Pole. I'm only going to Scotland, and I lived there a good part of my life."

"Not the part that matters," said Mama.

Papa laughed. "You mean the part I spent with you."

"The part in which you raised a family and made something of yourself instead of being nothing but a poor Scottish boy."

"The world is filled with poor Scottish boys," said Papa, "making things of themselves. Carnegie, for example."

"Every time I say something against Scotland, you and all your friends come right up with Carnegie. Just as though there isn't a bit of difference between Carnegie and Ferguson, or Carnegie and Frazer, or Carnegie and Joseph MacLean."

"I don't like to leave you and the children," said Papa.

"Nonsense. This won't be your first trip and it won't be your last either."

Papa hesitated for a moment. "You know," he said quietly, too quietly for Mama's taste, "it will be my last trip home, though. I'm too old to go through all this turmoil and torment again."

"It's a wonder you haven't been there before. It's almost as though it's a land that doesn't exist for you any more."

"It's there on the map," said Papa. "And it's there in my past. But the map and my past have been washed out by so many years; by all that expanse of ocean. It's hard even to remember why I want to see it again."

"It's home, that's why," said Mama. "If I were never to see Shrewsbury again; if I were never to see the way the river sputters against that little stretch of sand there by Seven Mile Bridge; if I were never to eat one Shrewsbury soft-shell crab again after it's steeped in brine the way old Mr. Edwards wraps it in that silky seaweed—wherever does he get that seaweed anyway, Joe?—if I were never to sit underneath my cherry tree again, there would be a whole part of me that would be just as dead as that old tree in the front yard is dead."

She sighed. "When a black cherry tree goes, it goes forever."

"I don't think there's a black cherry tree in all of Scotland," said Papa. "It's hard to remember even what there was in Scotland, except Glasga and Edinburgh and lots of streets and lots of rocks. Aye, and lots of water. I'm afraid, Bertha, for me it's mostly ghosties and ghoulies and things that go bump in the night. The things that really go bump in the night are our own memories, and the ghosties are those dreams of so long ago and far away, when we were such wee bairns that all the world and our mothers hovered over us, guarded us, kept us warm. Yes, I guess I had better have my winter coat after all. I can remember how cold we were, even in the summer."

"Hunger," said Mama. "It was probably hunger as well as anything. Until I met you, I don't think you ever had a decent meal to eat."

"But I had a good cup of tea, Mama," said Papa. "We always had a good cup of tea."

"You drank the whole Atlantic in your cups of tea," said Mama, "but you were never able to get home that way. It's too bad you wouldn't like to try the airplane. That would be a real sport."

"I came by water and I'm going home by water."

"Can't you go direct? Why do you have to go via Dublin with Mr. Dolan?"

"He's a good Irishman," said Papa. "And it's been years since I've seen Dublin. It's a fine city."

"It's nothing but cockles and mussels to me," said Mama. "I'm sure it's as cold as the rest of the old world. Everybody that ever comes from there is cold and hungry, from all that I can see. There must have been a depression there since the time of Adam. They can't support them all, that's the truth, and as soon as the depression is over, then there's a war brewing. I can tell you, Joe, I can feel it in my bones. My grandmother felt it in her bones and there was the Civil War, and I can remember Mama saying to me on one vacation down here, years ago, there's going to be a war and they'll take your boy, and they did take him." She hesitated for a moment, thinking of her son.

"I can feel it in my bones now; they're getting older now, my bones, but I can feel in them just as strongly; maybe even more sharply because I am older. There'll be a war, Joseph. Don't get caught in it. You were caught in Japan in 1914, remember, and all the trouble and horror of getting back."

"I know what I'm doing, Bertha. At least I know what I'm doing about taking a boat and not getting caught in a war or anything like that. That Hitler won't try anything; he's all noise, I think."

"That Mussolini is all fancy steps and gestures," said Mama, "but put them both together, the gestures and the noise, and those two no-goods will step right into trouble and take us all with them."

"Well, I'll have this summer anyway," said Papa. "Although I must confess the last of any decade fills one with a certain kind of dread. I remember 1919 and then 1929—oh, they roll around fast now, Bertha, because we're getting older, I guess. I wonder if anybody will ever remember this year— 1939."

"I'll remember it," said Mama, "because it's the year you finally got to see your home again . . . "

Papa and Mr. Dolan sailed straight to the harbor of Cobh. It took them forever to get from Cobh to Dublin and during that time, Papa wrote, he had heard more about the Irish than he ever desired to hear again. "For the last five days," explained Papa in his letter home, "we dined in a different place every night, and there is nothing to beat the Shelburne, but Dolan, God bless him, is going around collecting menus like a crazy man. If there were a menu for the Last Supper, Dolan would be picking it up, pocketing it, and buying a frame for it. All our street will be papered with the pasteboard of Dolan's palate if he keeps this up."

The days went on, and for a long time we heard nothing from the travelers. At least it seemed a long time, but it couldn't have been more than two weeks or so. Mama, who was used to Papa's long trips, did not grow as impatient as we children did. We waited impatiently for some picture postcard or an airmail letter, because, although we were now adolescents, the mystery of other places was still strong and, to pin down Papa's very reality, we needed a slip of paper or a card.

Papa's world had changed; he knew it and he was trying to find out just how it had changed. Our world, on the other hand, was changing so rapidly that we could not hope to find out today, tomorrow, next week, or even next year, who we were or where we were going. Our full identities were yet to come, were yet to be reached, as though some part of us had yet to evolve like history that had yet to be written. In the meantime it became apparent that history was more and more around us.

That summer was a strange one. There was for me the day-to-day reality of College Boards. That was the immediate future. That future occupied only part of my mind. The rest was in that very distant past where for a while, step by step, I walked with Papa into a country of romance. Were all the moors covered with heather, were all the Scottish islands diadems in cold seas? Were all the Scottish heroes resplendent in plaid? Were all the bannocks finer and smoother than ever could be made in America? Was the toffee more chewy? Was Edinburgh more beautiful than New York? Were the people hospitable? Were the people kind, clever, wise?

What was it like to be a MacLean going home to the MacLean country?

I fired note after note off to Papa, but as a traveler he was far too busy to answer, or far too burdened with catching trains, seeing old friends, old relatives, and chasing old dreams that were never to be caught again. Those dreams were like Burns's poem, and I hummed it and sang it throughout the house all that summer. " 'My heart's in the Highlands,' " I sang. " 'My heart is not here. My heart's in the Highlands, a'chasing the deer.' "

Eventually Mama became downright distressed. "It's obvious," she said bitterly, "that your heart's not here. I've never seen you moping around so, Seon, in my life."

Finally we had a long letter. "Things," wrote Papa, "started to go wrong when we hit Dublin. You know how hipped Dolan is on that Gaelic of his. Surely English is a glorious language, but obviously it's never been enough for a MacAllister or a Dolan. We barely hit the coast of Ireland before Dolan let loose the greatest flurry of Irish that ever hit the ears of those good people.

"A funny thing, you know, in Ireland we did not hear one Irish-American voice. It's almost as though we were exiles here, and I speak for myself as well, because now I've been in Scotland long enough to realize that my voice, my heart, and my life have changed. We exiles speak with some tongue of our own, some ancient, distant language that, like wine, was unable to cross the mountains. Gaelic, you know, was one of those languages. It never crossed the barriers of time and space. Here in Scotland and Ireland you find tiny, cut-off pockets of the world where a wee bit of Gaelic—a 'good morning' or a 'God be with you'—comes to your ear.

"God, of course," continued Papa, "is not with me. It's just Dolan, and he thinks he's all the ancient Irish gods himself, or at least he thought so until he had his comeuppance on the streets of Dublin. As I think about it, it's a sad story. Although I get a little wicked laughter out of it, I feel sorry for Dolan and for the likes of us who go chasing the deer of our memory with the Lloyd and Haig shoes that we wear today. The cut of our suits is different, the material is different, the entire fabric of our life is different. Still here we go in the faded tartans of yesterday, chasing some old past so overgrown with weeds that none of us can ever find it again."

When Papa returned to New York, he grew even more philosophical, but he had enjoyed the high comedy of what he called, "Dolan's Adventures in Ireland."

It had been Dolan's ambition to visit every section of the Gaeltacht, in both Ireland and Scotland. The Gaeltacht were those little sections of the world cut off by history and by geography from the English-speaking areas.

Over the years, Mr. Dolan had often fascinated me with his discussion of those isolated spots of perfection, where the peat that warmed the hearth was the finest peat in the world, and the feet that walked the roads were the finest feet in the world, and the tongues that chattered, chattered (for they were all great talkers, said Dolan) were the finest, nimblest, noblest in all the world. "Once to the Gaeltacht, lassie, and you'll know a bit of heaven, the like of which you've never seen before."

Dolan had told Papa, "You can warm your hands at the hearth of a Gaelic language. It will bring back color to your cheek and magic to your world; believe me, Joe, you've got to see the Gaeltacht."

"I was born in the heart of it, you forget," grumbled Papa.

"But you lost your Gaelic."

"There was a time there," said Papa, "when one had a choice between losing one's Gaelic or losing one's breeks. In the long run, I decided that I would make it in the world with the tongue of the English rather than parading myself like a jay bird forever in the cold waters of the Irish Sea."

Dolan had been very convincing, and for that reason Papa decided to make an extended tour with him throughout all of Ireland's counties. He could visit Bride in Ulster and then painfully, perilously, as with all pilgrimages, make his way home to Glasgow and his Islands.

That was the way Papa and Dolan planned the trip in the spring as they unfolded maps and charts, letters of introduction, and letters of old friends, covering the library table with the paper magic of the summer.

That summer now had come and gone; Papa had warmed himself at the hearth of Irish history, chilled himself in the mist of his own Scotland.

177

"I wouldn't go declaring," he said to Ferguson, "that it was a ghastly disaster. No, I wouldn't go that far at all. It's just that perhaps I'm getting too old for travel, the kind of travel you have to make adaptations to all the time."

"Nonsense," said Ferguson. "Look at the way you took off only a year ago to Hong Kong."

"Well, that was business," said Papa. "Business is a steadying influence; I know when I'm looking for a cup of tea or a bit of spice, but when I'm looking for something that, glory be, must have been lost in the waters of the past a long time ago, my feet are as clumsy as an islandman's in a pair of pampooties."

"I wish you had brought me some pampooties," Gogo said, coming into the room.

"Nonsense," said Papa. "If the islanders haven't figured out a way to make a real shoe and have to go swishing and swashing around in the waves in a piece of twisted old leather (it takes the family a night to bite them through to make them soft enough to wear the next day; they're worse than the Eskimos, they are), if people haven't discovered that, there is no hope for them.

"You stick to those nice black patent-leather shoes, Gogo, and I don't want to hear anything more about pampooties in the house.

"The one that the trip was a real blow to," said Papa, looking down carefully at his shoe to be sure that it was garbed in the leather of civilization, "the one that it was really a blow to was Dolan. I don't think he'll ever recover from it.

"We are all wild geese, Ferguson—the Scots, and the Irish.

Aye, for that matter, the Italians, the Jews; they were all great wanderers on the earth. There is a poignancy about the Irish deeper than in the rest of us, because I think their dreams are made up from landscapes and such unrealities that there is no hope for them until they get a couple of generations away from that rough green turf."

"There will be one of them President yet," said Ferguson. "You can just tell it by the way they go about in streetcars and politics, mark my words."

"We were strolling down O'Connell Street, frisky as Irish colts, and it came upon Dolan that he must make a holy call to the post office," said Papa. "It's not enough that you go to the post office to mail a letter in Ireland; you go to pay obeisance to those glorious men who fell in the Easter Rising. As soon as Dolan got inside the door," said Papa, "his Irish came thick and fast; there was no chance of getting an English word out of him. He went up to a clerk, speaking only Irish, asking for an airmail stamp. She was a wee lass and none too bright. But Irish law demands that civil servants know their Irish well. Maybe she was twisting his tail a bit. He'd ask in Irish and she'd reply, 'What do you want?' in English. He was so hot and indignant that he was going to report her right up to the President of the Dail. The girl, for a while there, was frightened with the fierceness of him. Most people don't realize how fierce and troubled the absentee patriot is. I thought he'd have a fit there, right on the floor, and those hives came out faster than the rain can block the sun on an Irish summer day. When we got outside, Dolan was a beaten man.

"We were soon followed by a bunch of youngsters, a bedraggled, tattered lot if there ever was, and Dolan, beaten, would not admit defeat. He wanted to turn around, I could feel him wanting to as I did myself—turn around and tell those kids to beat it, stop hanging on our coattails and making us nervous. I couldn't figure out what kind of mischief they were up to, but it was some kind of teasing torment they were apt to give poor Dolan. He was itching from his hives and itching to get back to the hotel and itching to get far away from everything that plagued him. He asked me the time, but I didn't have it and he stood there, stockstill. Then he turned on his heels and, for a few moments, the kids there were frightened. And then he asked 'em in a ringing Irish as was ever declared from the noble Irish Senate, 'What time is it?'

"The kids were startled for a moment, but then started screaming, 'There's that Irish-speaking Yank, Irish-speaking Yank." Papa sighed. "Poor Dolan found out what time it was. It was too late to ever go home again, far too late."

"And what about Scotland?" Ferguson asked.

"It's still there," said Papa, "but let me tell you something, Ferguson. We're not. We're here. They can take all that lord of the isles and that kind of nonsense and dump it in Little Minch. There isn't one man of us that shouldn't be happy enough to be what we are."

"Lords of Manhattan Isle," said Ferguson, preening himself.

"Aye," said Papa sadly, "but over there" (and over there had all the poignancy of far away and long ago, of home, and mother, and sisters and brothers in another world, and a whole lifetime), "over there, they *used* to make a fine cup of tea."

the foot upon the floor

The neighborhood has dispersed. The old friends are gone. The streets have changed. My childhood has been carefully folded in old tartans and put away. In a small way, I have been a shanachie—as my people were before me —storytellers, narrators of some distant past. I sing of an old New York clan, of chieftains of long ago, of an ancient poetry of living.

Once, long after I stepped across the threshold of maturity, I put, as John Keats said, my foot upon the floor. That floor of yesterday, worn by old memory, splintered with old sorrow, polished with many lives, seemed to find its foundation in a visit to Robert Burns's birthplace in Scotland itself.

It seemed as though every Scot in the world was making a pilgrimage to Ayr during the Burns bicentennial. As we stood in line to enter his birthplace, we were a motley crew: all ages, all kinds of accents, all sorts of memories. I looked up into the sky—blue and cloudless—it did not seem a Scottish day at all. In New York we could have a series of such perfect days: the buildings piercing the skies, the skies piercing the eye with color, dimension, texture, and expanse—all so familiar that it did not impress itself freshly on the palette of memory. But this scene was quite different. One stumbled over memories—this country was made up of memories—some large, some small, some smooth, some harsh, as surely as the walk beneath our feet was composed of pebbles. The largest memory of all was Papa reading, reciting, breathing, yes, living Burns. Robert Burns, dear Burns. The small memories were of the wee beastie and the wee cottage.

It was too warm for sweaters and jackets, but the Scots have a general suspicion of their country's weather. It is a well-founded distrust and, although that spring was rich with golden days, no one could quite believe it. A trip to the Burns Cottage was just right for this nearly summer day.

"Dinky, keep your sweater on," parents on holiday muttered or screamed at their offending offspring. "Ah, let me alone," children on holiday screamed and muttered at their offending parents.

Two small children climbed on top of the guidepost. One tottered on top of the sign that spelled out *To the Birthplace.* Dinky, surely it was Dinky (with his sweater off), hung from his knees from the directional arrow that read *To the Museum of Relics.*

"It's them that makes the relics," a bystander informed me.

"It's nippers like those that makes relics and rubbish out of everything. Glasgow slummers. Look at them kicking up the turf. They'll ruin the garden, sure. What a nice piece of land."

It was indeed a nice piece of land. The grass was a green welcome, the flowers luxuriant. They disturbed my memories with their carefree blooms. It just didn't seem possible that this was land that Burns ever knew. And it wasn't possible. For nearly two hundred years the Scots have been ripening and improving that plot of land that so nearly defeated the Burns family.

"Oh, indeed," Papa had told me over and over again, "it was a mean cruel strip of soil if ever there was a plot of misery. The Burns family always had it hard. They left one miserable farm for another. Someday you'll get to Galloway and you'll see with your own eyes."

So here I was—seeing with my own eyes, and sharing those eyes with Papa until I was astigmatic from focusing on the past so that the present blurred, focusing on the present so that the past faded.

"Dinky, I told you before!"

What did this scene mean to Dinky? I wondered. Did it have any meaning? Was it just a day in the country? Beside Glasgow, etched, framed, and carved out of the blackness of the atmosphere, this Galloway day was light, sunshine, and youth. There was something so young about this very spot, so youthful about this pilgrimage.

Burns himself had not lived here beyond his boyhood, a lad no older than Dinky, a boy storing up his country's songs, soils, sorrows, pleasures—swallowing them whole, the way he would later gorge himself on life.

Suddenly, Burns was very much alive. I could see him, scratched on my mind in tight, thin lines, just as he appeared on the engraving in Papa's room. The Poet himself bent over, one hand still clutching the plow, the other hand unearthing the mouse in her nest.

Who was the wee tim'rous mouse? Burns himself looked kind of mousy in the picture. Sometimes he was very much alive to me, but at other times he was quite dead and the outlandish tongue of his verse grated on my ear. I harbored the thought that all Scots were a little peculiar. Certainly some of their words were strange. I'd never understand the variety of accents that I heard right at home as Papa's friends came and went, an endless file of nostalgic tea guests.

"It's a queer tongue," Mama once volunteered, hoping, I'm sure, that Papa would make her feel less an outsider. But Papa, who was so frequently all sympathy, who understood one far more, far faster, far better than one could ever hope for, had no such support for Mama's confusion over his friends.

"There's nane sa quair as folk," said Papa.

"You and your folks," said Mama. "You're right all right. There's none as queer as *your* folk."

" 'O ye whose cheek the tear of pity stains,' " Papa chanted. " 'Draw near with pious rev'rence and attend'!' "

When I heard him boom out like that I attended well. It was just as I figured—most Scots talked in riddles or poetry, just like Papa.

Here lie the loving husband's dear remains,
The tender father, and the gen'rous friend.

"Just what is *that* nonsense," said Mama, wiping the crumbs free from the table with the palm of her hand.

"That, my woman," Papa said, "is the epitaph of Scotland's greatest poet."

"Papa!" I cried out.

"Yes, lassie," he said quietly, his temper having been cooled by poetry.

"Papa," I said, wanting so much to pick up those words, to glue them together into a prism of understanding. "Papa, tell me the truth? Did Robert Burns kill that mouse?"

"What mouse, lassie?"

"That wee beastie, Papa, the little mouse with all the babies. Did he hurt them with the plow? You know, like the picture in your room."

Papa smiled. "Burns never hurt a thing, child. Least of all a wee beastie."

That was such a small memory to encounter years later in this unfamiliar countryside. Because it was unfamiliar; only the Burns Cottage itself looked familiar, and that too was all out of perspective. I first knew the cottage as a toy. Papa had given me a tiny pottery copy of it—barely an inch long, washed white as moonlight with a gash of colored thatch as the roof. It looked less like a toy than a piece of candy. Scottish marzipan for an exile's granddaughter. The food of home to renew the spirit. I was an American cast in a different mold, but the clay or whatever it was that formed my childhood was Papa's clay. And here I was, the year of the Burns bicentennial, outside of that cottage, now grown to its full size as I had grown, gaining entrance into my own past for a bare shilling.

It was an "auld clay biggin"—a hut, without a doubt. The dampness of the old clay, the dampness of an old heritage clung with a mossy closeness once we were inside the cottage. I had on high heels and I felt momentarily trapped in the cobbled entranceway, as we are always in some curious way trapped in our past.

"Ma, I'm cold!" cried the boy Dinky.

"Shut yer mouth," answered his mother. "Your father's giving us a lovely holiday."

"It smells," replied Dinky.

It did, too. And it was moldy, fiercely cold, as raw as any cathedral. And almost as sanctified. Even Dinky didn't raise his voice above a whisper once inside the kitchen. It was here that "blast o' Janwar' win' blew Hansel" when Burns was born. I knew that blast. My sister and I were both January children, and Papa had recited those lines on every birthday. It was things like that that made the Scots queer, I had thought. But I thought that no longer. If one had felt that blast of "Janwar" wind within this room, only poetry could ever warm the body again.

We gawked at the bed in which Burns was born, we tripped over the rope that protected the milking stool, we studied the washing tub, an old grate, and Betty Burns's trunk. The boy Dinky managed to get a piece of splinter in his hand, that supposedly came from the piece of oak carefully preserved from the Auld Brig of Ayr. Dinky didn't seem to care much one way or another.

"I wanna go."

So did the rest of us. We came out into the sunlight.

Later, I gave my daughter the little replica of the Burns Cottage. I passed on to her, and she will pass on to her children some of my and my ancestors' old dreams, and I hear her singing now:

My heart's in the Highlands
My heart is not here
My heart's in the Highlands
A'chasing the deer.

The time has come for her to hunt her own tomorrow.